It's easy to get lost in the cancer world

Let NCCN Guidelines for Patients® be your guide

✓ Step-by-step guides to the cancer care options likely to have the best results

✓ Based on treatment guidelines used by health care providers worldwide

✓ Designed to help you discuss cancer treatment with your doctors

National Comprehensive
Cancer Network®

NCCN Guidelines for Patients® are developed by the National Comprehensive Cancer Network® (NCCN®)

NCCN

✓ An alliance of leading cancer centers across the United States devoted to patient care, research, and education

Cancer centers that are part of NCCN:
NCCN.org/cancercenters

NCCN Clinical Practice Guidelines in Oncology (NCCN Guidelines®)

✓ Developed by experts from NCCN cancer centers using the latest research and years of experience

✓ For providers of cancer care all over the world

✓ Expert recommendations for cancer screening, diagnosis, and treatment

Free online at
NCCN.org/guidelines

NCCN Guidelines for Patients

✓ Present information from the NCCN Guidelines in an easy-to-learn format

✓ For people with cancer and those who support them

✓ Explain the cancer care options likely to have the best results

Free online at
NCCN.org/patientguidelines

These NCCN Guidelines for Patients are based on the NCCN Guidelines® for Colon Cancer, Version 1.2022 – February 25, 2022.

NCCN Foundation seeks to support the millions of patients and their families affected by a cancer diagnosis by funding and distributing NCCN Guidelines for Patients. NCCN Foundation is also committed to advancing cancer treatment by funding the nation's promising doctors at the center of innovation in cancer research. For more details and the full library of patient and caregiver resources, visit NCCN.org/patients.

National Comprehensive Cancer Network (NCCN) / NCCN Foundation
3025 Chemical Road, Suite 100
Plymouth Meeting, PA 19462
215.690.0300

NATIONAL COMPREHENSIVE CANCER NETWORK®
FOUNDATION
Guiding Treatment. Changing Lives.

NCCN Guidelines for Patients are supported by funding from the NCCN Foundation®

To make a gift or learn more, please visit NCCNFoundation.org/donate
or e-mail PatientGuidelines@NCCN.org.

Additional support provided by

The Anal Cancer Foundation (ACF) is dedicated to ending anal cancer and improving the lives of those affected by it. ACF programs raise awareness, accelerate early detection, improve quality of life, and support research to find a cure. ACF is proud to partner with the NCCN Foundation to provide this comprehensive, evidence-based guide to support colon cancer patients and their loved ones. For help during any stage of your journey, please visit analcancerfoundation.org.

The Colorectal Cancer Alliance is the largest nonprofit advocacy organization dedicated to colorectal cancer. The Alliance empowers a nation of allies who work with us to support patients and families, caregivers, and survivors; to raise awareness of preventive measures; and inspire efforts to fund critical research. Call the toll-free Helpline for support and resources: 877.422.2030 ccalliance.org

Fight Colorectal Cancer We fight to cure colorectal cancer and serve as relentless champions of hope for all affected by this disease through informed patient support, impactful policy change, and breakthrough research endeavors. As an organization dedicated to helping the community find trusted resources to make informed decisions about their health, we are proud to support this comprehensive resource. fightcolorectalcancer.org

Contents

1
Colon cancer basics

Colon cancer is a common and highly treatable cancer. Advances in screening and treatment have led to better outcomes for patients. This chapter provides some basic information about colon cancer that will help prepare you for treatment.

The colon

The colon is the longest part of the large intestine, also known as the large bowel. The large bowel is a long tube-shaped organ that forms the last part of the digestive system. The digestive system breaks down food for the body to use.

After being swallowed, food passes through the esophagus and into the stomach, where it is turned into a liquid. From the stomach, food enters the small intestine. Here food is broken down into very small parts to allow nutrients to be absorbed into the bloodstream. Partly digested food then moves into the colon.

The colon

The colon is the first and longest part of the large bowel. The colon absorbs water from unused food, turning it into stool. Stool is held in the last section of the large bowel, called the rectum, until it exits the body through the anus.

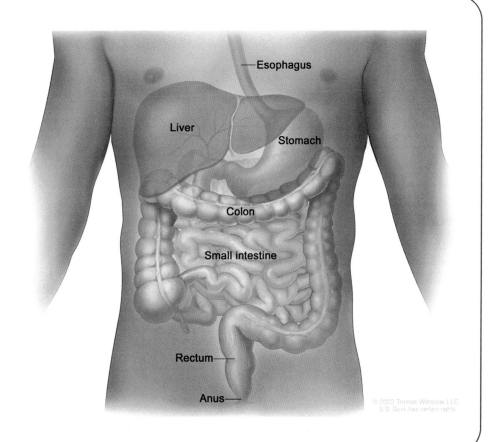

Esophagus

Liver

Stomach

Colon

Small intestine

Rectum

Anus

© 2022 Terese Winslow LLC
U.S. Govt. has certain rights

The colon is the first and longest section of the large bowel. It is almost 5 feet long and has four parts: the ascending, transverse, descending, and sigmoid colon.

The first part of the colon is called the cecum. This pouch is about the size of a small orange. Sticking out from the cecum is a skinny tube called the appendix. It is closed at one end, and is about the size of a finger.

In the colon, water is absorbed from unused food, changing it from a liquid to a solid. This solid, unused food is called feces or stool. Stool then moves into the last section of the large bowel, called the rectum. Stool is held in the rectum until it exits the body through an opening called the anus.

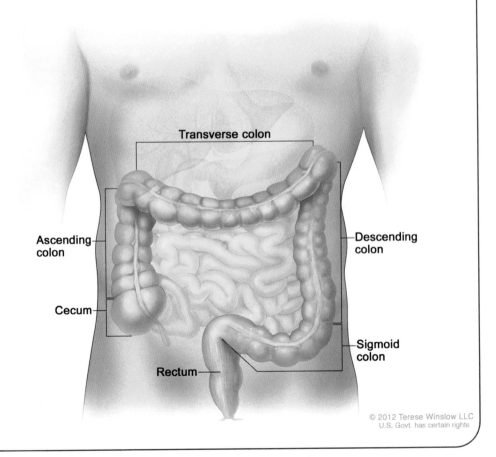

Parts of the colon

The colon is the longest part of the large bowel. It is almost 5 feet long and has four sections: the ascending, transverse, descending, and sigmoid colon.

Transverse colon

Ascending colon

Descending colon

Cecum

Rectum

Sigmoid colon

© 2012 Terese Winslow LLC
U.S. Govt. has certain rights

Colon polyps

A polyp is an overgrowth of cells on the inner lining of the colon wall. There are different types of polyps. Some types are more likely to turn into cancer than others. The most common type is called an adenoma. Adenomas are considered pre-cancerous. While it may take many years, adenomas can become invasive colon cancer. Cancer that forms in an adenoma is known as an adenocarcinoma. Adenocarcinoma is the most common type of colon cancer. Polyps that rarely turn into cancer include hyperplastic and inflammatory polyps.

Removing polyps can prevent cancer before it starts. Polyps can also be tested to make sure that cancer has not already started to develop. While most polyps do not become cancer, almost all colon cancers start in a polyp. Most polyps can be removed during a colonoscopy using a minor surgical procedure called a polypectomy. More information on colon polyps is provided in *Part 4: Non-metastatic cancer*.

Staging

The cancer stage describes the extent of cancer in the body. It is used to plan which tests may be needed and which treatments are best for you. Having a general idea of the structure of the colon wall is helpful for understanding how colon cancer is staged.

The colon wall is made of layers of tissue. Cancer starts in the innermost layer that comes in contact with food. This layer is called the mucosa. The next layer is the submucosa. It is made of connective tissue and contains mucus glands, blood and lymph vessels, and nerves. The submucosa is followed by a layer of muscle called the muscularis propria. The outer, fourth layer is called serosa (or adventitia).

If left untreated, cancer cells grow through the layers of the colon wall, towards the inside of the abdomen. The cancer can then invade structures or organs outside of the colon. Cancer cells can also break off from the colon tumor and travel through lymph or blood to nearby lymph nodes.

The American Joint Committee on Cancer (AJCC) tumor, node, metastasis (TNM) system is used to stage colon cancer. In the AJCC system, the following key pieces of information about the cancer are used to give it a stage:

> **T:** How far the tumor has grown into or through the colon wall

> **N:** Whether any lymph nodes have cancer

> **M:** Whether the cancer has spread to areas or organs outside the colon (metastasized)

The T, N, and M scores are combined to assign the cancer a stage. There are 5 stages of colon cancer. They are numbered 0, I (1), II (2), III (3), or IV (4). The stages are explained below.

Stage 0

There are abnormal cells on the innermost layer of the colon wall. These abnormal cells may become cancer and spread into deeper layers of the colon wall. Stage 0 colon cancer is also called carcinoma in situ of the colon.

Stage I

The cancer has grown into either the second or third layer of the colon wall. There is no cancer in nearby lymph nodes or in areas outside the colon.

Stage II

The cancer has grown into, or beyond, the fourth layer of the colon wall. There is no cancer in nearby lymph nodes or in areas outside the colon.

Stage III

The cancer has spread from the colon to nearby lymph nodes or there are tumor deposits. Tumor deposits are small tumors in the fat around the colon.

Stage IV

The cancer has spread to areas outside the colon and nearby lymph nodes. Colon cancer spreads most often to the liver and/or lungs.

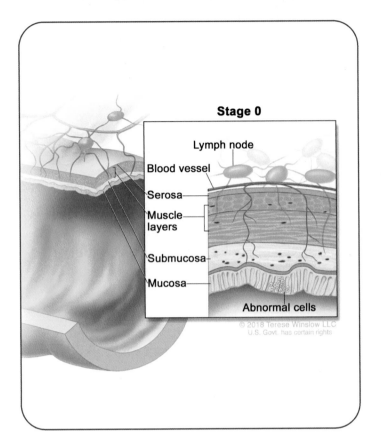

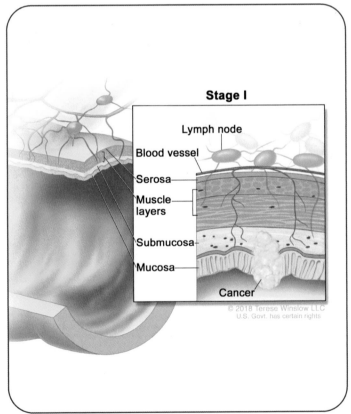

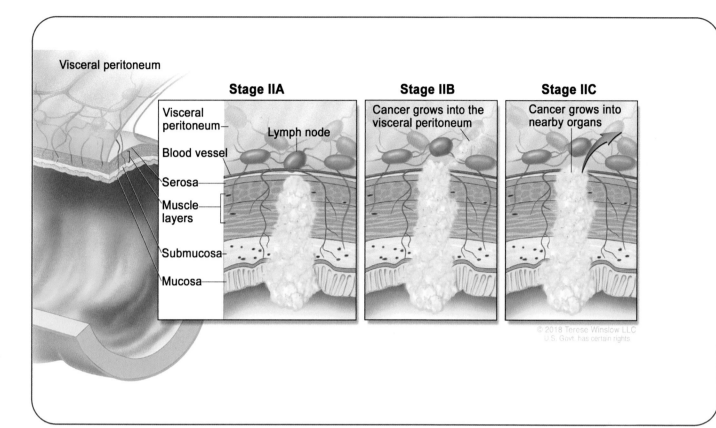

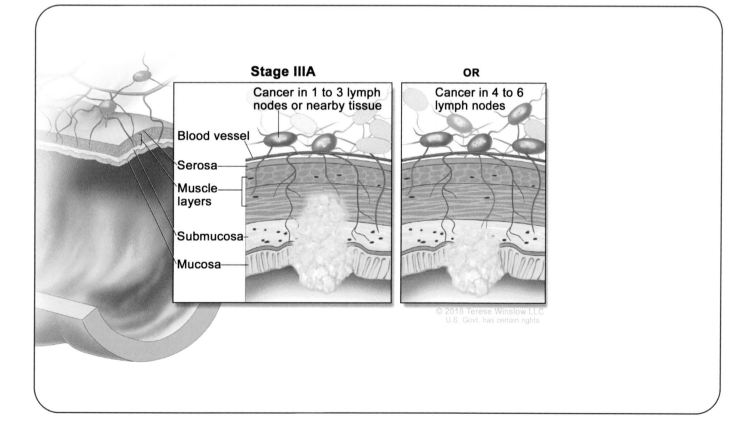

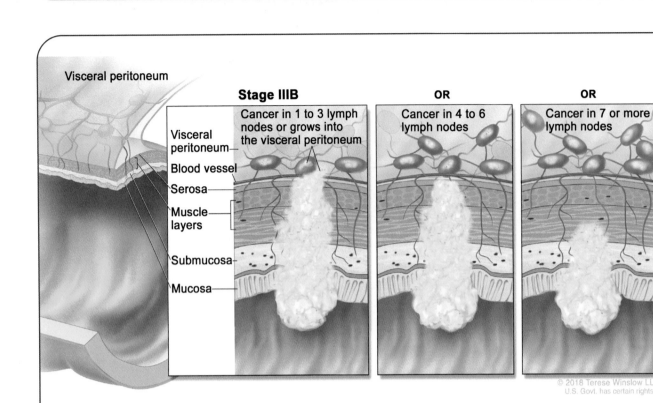

Visceral peritoneum

Stage IIIB

Visceral peritoneum
Blood vessel
Serosa
Muscle layers
Submucosa
Mucosa

Cancer in 1 to 3 lymph nodes or grows into the visceral peritoneum

OR

Cancer in 4 to 6 lymph nodes

OR

Cancer in 7 or more lymph nodes

© 2018 Terese Winslow LLC
U.S. Govt. has certain rights

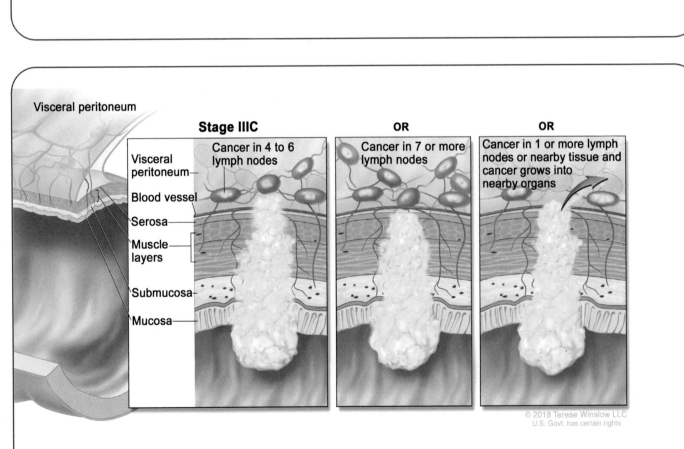

Visceral peritoneum

Stage IIIC

Visceral peritoneum
Blood vessel
Serosa
Muscle layers
Submucosa
Mucosa

Cancer in 4 to 6 lymph nodes

OR

Cancer in 7 or more lymph nodes

OR

Cancer in 1 or more lymph nodes or nearby tissue and cancer grows into nearby organs

© 2018 Terese Winslow LLC
U.S. Govt. has certain rights

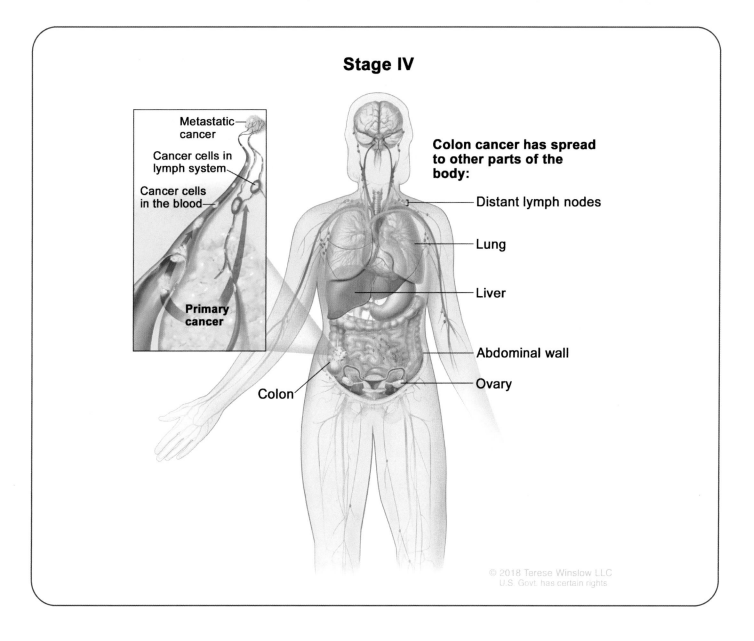

Stage IV

Metastatic cancer

Cancer cells in lymph system

Cancer cells in the blood

Primary cancer

Colon

Colon cancer has spread to other parts of the body:

Distant lymph nodes

Lung

Liver

Abdominal wall

Ovary

© 2018 Terese Winslow LLC
U.S. Govt. has certain rights

Key points

- The colon is the first and longest part of the large bowel.

- The colon has four parts: the ascending, transverse, descending, and sigmoid colon.

- Most colon cancers start in polyps called adenomas.

- If left untreated, cancer grows through the colon wall towards the inside of the abdomen.

- Cancer cells can spread to other body parts through lymph or blood. This is called metastasis.

- The stage is an assessment of the extent of cancer in the body.

2
Treatment planning

Your doctors will make a treatment plan just for you. First, they need to gather information about your unique cancer and your general health. This chapter discusses testing and other steps needed to create your treatment plan.

Health history

Your personal health history includes any health events and medicines you've taken in your life. It helps your doctors decide which treatments may be best for you. Colon cancer and other diseases can run in families. For this reason, your doctor will also ask about your family health history. It is helpful to know who in your family has had what diseases and at what ages. Your doctor may ask about the health of your siblings, your parents and their siblings, and your grandparents and their siblings.

Inherited cancer syndromes

Colon cancer most often occurs for unknown reasons. Some people, however, are more likely to get colon cancer than the average person. This is because a mutation in their DNA was passed down to them, causing a disorder that increases the risk of colon cancer. This is called an inherited cancer syndrome. Most colon cancers associated with an inherited cancer syndrome are due to either Lynch syndrome or familial adenomatous polyposis (FAP). Both are uncommon in people with colon cancer. There are several other inherited syndromes that are even less common.

If your doctor thinks you might have an inherited syndrome, you will be referred to a genetic counselor. A genetic counselor can talk with you and sometimes your family members about getting tested for syndromes related to colon cancer. To be tested, you must provide a sample of blood or saliva. A pathologist tests the sample for changes (mutations) in genes that cause these syndromes. It is important to meet with a genetic counselor before having any genetic testing.

Lynch syndrome

People born with Lynch syndrome are at high risk of developing colon cancer and some other cancers, particularly endometrial and ovarian cancers. This syndrome is caused by inherited mutations of genes that fix damaged DNA. These are called mismatch repair (MMR) genes. NCCN experts recommend testing everyone with colon cancer for problems with the MMR genes. This helps determine who should be tested for Lynch syndrome. Only about 5 out of every 100 people with colon cancer have Lynch syndrome. Sometimes Lynch syndrome is referred to as hereditary non-polyposis colon cancer (HNPCC), but they are not exactly the same. Specific family history criteria must be met in order for a diagnosis of HNPCC to be made.

Familial adenomatous polyposis

FAP is a rare inherited syndrome. It can cause hundreds to thousands of polyps to form in the colon and rectum. The polyps start as benign (non-cancerous) growths, but over time they can turn into colon cancer. Cancer is likely to develop by age 50 in people with classic FAP. A milder form called attenuated FAP causes fewer polyps and usually starts later in life. Only about 1 in 100 people with colon cancer have FAP.

Colonoscopy

A colonoscopy is a procedure that allows your doctor to examine your colon for polyps and lesions that may be cancerous. A colonoscope is the device used for the test. Part of it looks like a thin tube. It has a light and camera. This part will be inserted into your anus and gently guided through the large bowel until it reaches the cecum.

You may be put on a liquid diet for 1 to 3 days before the test. You may also take a laxative or an enema the night before. This will clean out your bowel. Right before the test, you may be given a sedative to lessen any pain. You will likely wear a hospital gown. The test will be performed while you lie on your side.

To see better, gas may be pumped into your bowel to make it bigger. You may be asked to shift a little to help your doctor guide the device. A picture of your colon will be viewed by your doctor on a screen. If a polyp is found, a cutting tool will be inserted through the tube to remove it. This is known as a polypectomy.

A colonoscopy takes about 30 to 60 minutes. Afterward, you may stay for another hour for any drugs that were used to wear off. However, you'll still need someone to drive you home. The next day, you will likely feel normal. Contact your doctor if you have severe pain, vomiting, bloody stool, or weakness.

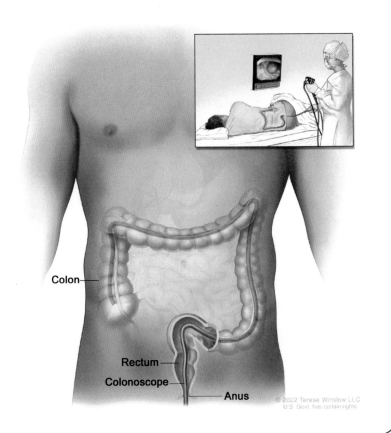

Colonoscopy

A colonoscopy is a procedure that allows your doctor to see and remove any abnormal tissue from the colon. A thin device is inserted through the anus, up the rectum, and into the colon. The device has a light, a camera, and a cutting tool.

Colon

Rectum

Colonoscope

Anus

© 2022 Terese Winslow LLC
U.S. Govt. has certain rights

Biopsy

A biopsy involves removing small pieces of tissue from the colon. A biopsy of a polyp or of suspected colon cancer is usually done during a colonoscopy. The samples are sent to a pathologist for testing.

If the cancer is suspected to have spread to areas outside the colon, such as the liver or lungs, a needle may be used to do the biopsy. In this case, a computed tomography (CT) scan or ultrasound may be used to help guide the needle into the tumor in order to remove the tissue sample. You might hear this referred to as a fine-needle aspiration (FNA).

Each time tissue is removed from the body and tested for cancer, the findings are detailed in a document called a pathology report. One key finding included in the report is the cancer grade, which is different than the cancer stage.

The cancer grade is a score of how fast the cancer is expected to grow and spread. It is based on how abnormal the cancer cells look when viewed under a microscope. Higher scores mean that the cancer is likely to grow and spread quickly. There are 5 possible grades:

- **GX** means that the grade cannot be determined.

- **G1** means that the cancer cells look similar to healthy cells. Also called well differentiated or low grade.

- **G2** means that the cancer cells are somewhat different than healthy cells. Also called moderately differentiated or intermediate grade.

- **G3** means that the cancer cells barely look like healthy cells. Also called poorly differentiated or high grade.

- **G4** means that the cancer cells are very abnormal looking. These are the highest grade and typically grow and spread faster than lower grade tumors. Also called undifferentiated or high grade.

Review your pathology report(s) with your doctor. Ask questions if you don't understand. This information can be complex. It is also a good idea to get a copy of your pathology report(s) and take notes.

Blood tests

Blood tests are used to look for signs of disease. A needle will be inserted into your vein to remove a sample of blood. The needle may bruise your skin. You may feel dizzy from the blood draw. Your blood sample will be sent to a lab for testing.

Complete blood count

A complete blood count (CBC) measures the number of blood cells in a blood sample. It includes numbers of white blood cells, red blood cells, and platelets. White blood cells help the body fight infection. Red blood cells carry oxygen throughout the body. Platelets help wounds heal by forming blood clots. Cancer and other health problems can cause low or high blood cell counts.

Chemistry profile

Also known as a comprehensive metabolic panel (CMP), this test measures the level of certain substances in the blood, such as metabolites, electrolytes, and proteins. The levels of these substances provide information about how well your kidneys, liver, and other organs are working.

CEA blood test

Carcinoembryonic antigen (CEA) is a protein found in blood. It is considered a tumor marker. The level of CEA is often higher-than-normal in people with colon cancer, especially if the cancer has spread to other organs. Pregnant females and people who smoke may have higher CEA levels. Monitoring CEA can be helpful even when the cancer is only in the colon and the level is normal, because the level will rise if the cancer later spreads to other organs. However, monitoring CEA is not helpful for some people, even if the cancer has spread.

Imaging tests

Imaging tests make pictures of areas inside the body. They can show areas of cancer. This information helps your doctors stage the cancer and plan treatment.

A radiologist is a doctor who is an expert in interpreting these images. Your radiologist will convey the imaging results to your cancer doctor (oncologist). This information helps plan the next steps of care.

Your treatment team will tell you how to prepare for these tests. You may need to stop taking some medicines and stop eating and drinking for a few hours before the scan. Tell your team if you get nervous in tight spaces. You may be given a type of medicine called a sedative to help you relax.

Computed tomography (CT)

CT takes many pictures of areas inside the body using x-rays. A computer combines the x-rays to make one detailed picture. The picture is saved for later viewing by a radiologist. CT is the main imaging test used to learn the extent of colon cancer in the body. It can show areas of cancer in nearby and distant sites.

A substance called contrast will be used to make the pictures clearer. It will be injected into your vein and mixed with a liquid to drink. The contrast may cause you to feel flushed or get hives. Some people have an allergic reaction to contrast. Tell your doctor if you've had problems with contrast in the past.

During the scan you will lie face-up on a table that moves through a tunnel-like machine. You will be alone during the scan, but a technician will be nearby. You will be able to hear and talk to the technician at all times. You may hear buzzing or clicking during the scan.

PET

In select cases CT may be combined with positron emission tomography (PET). PET/CT is not often used for colon cancer. It may be used to help determine if surgery is an option for metastatic disease, or in the rare event that you cannot have contrast for CT or magnetic resonance imaging (MRI). PET involves first injecting a radioactive drug (a "sugar tracer") into the body. The radiotracer is detected with a special camera during the scan. Cancer cells appear brighter than normal cells because they use sugar more quickly.

MRI

MRI uses a magnetic field and radio waves to make pictures. It is not often used to plan treatment for colon cancer. Your doctor may order an MRI if the CT scan was unclear. MRI is most often used to get a better look at the liver or rectum if needed. Contrast should be used.

Getting an MRI is much like getting a CT scan. In some cases, the area of the body being imaged is placed within a narrowed coil device. The coil device looks like a brace. It covers your body from below your chest to the top of your legs. It sends and receives radio waves. Straps may be used to help you stay in place. An MRI may cause your body to feel a bit warm. If MRI is being used to better see

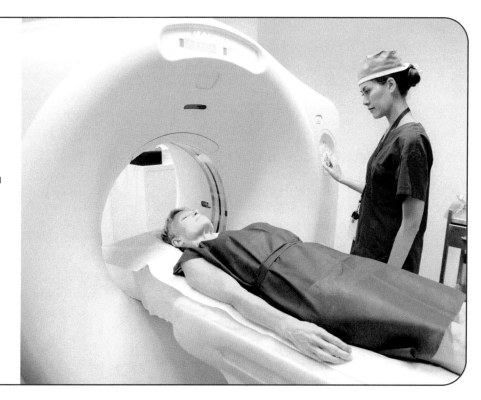

CT scan

CT with contrast is the main imaging test used to determine the extent of colon cancer in the body. CT takes many pictures of the inside of the body using x-rays. A computer combines the x-rays to make one detailed picture.

cancer near the rectum, an enema may be needed. Or, a gel may be inserted into the rectum beforehand.

Biomarker testing

Biomarkers are specific features of cancer cells. Biomarkers can include proteins made in response to the cancer and changes (mutations) in the DNA of the cancer cells.

Biomarker testing is used to learn whether your cancer has any targetable changes to help guide your treatment. If it does, targeted therapy or immunotherapy may be a treatment option if needed. The results of biomarker testing can also be used to determine whether you meet the criteria for joining certain clinical trials. Testing for biomarker mutations involves analyzing a piece of tumor tissue or a sample of blood in a lab.

Other names for biomarker testing include molecular testing, genomic testing, tumor gene testing, next-generation sequencing, and mutation testing. Biomarkers used for colon cancer treatment planning are described next.

For everyone with colon cancer

MMR/MSI testing
In normal cells, a process called mismatch repair (MMR) fixes errors (mutations) that happen when DNA divides and makes a copy of itself. If a cell's MMR system isn't working right, errors build up and cause the DNA to become unstable. This is called microsatellite instability (MSI).

There are two kinds of lab tests for this biomarker. Depending on the method used, an abnormal result is called either microsatellite instability high (MSI-H) or mismatch repair deficient (dMMR). Tumors that **are not** MSI-H/dMMR are referred to as microsatellite stable (MSS) or mismatch repair proficient (pMMR).

MMR or MSI testing is recommended for everyone diagnosed with colon cancer. If the cancer is dMMR/MSI-H, you will also be tested for Lynch syndrome.

For metastatic colon cancer

If colon cancer has spread to other parts of the body, such as the liver or lungs, testing for the tumor biomarkers described next is recommended. Testing for these biomarkers may be performed individually, or as part of a larger panel (group). Testing for many biomarkers at one time is called next-generation sequencing (NGS). NGS can find other, rare gene mutations for which targeted treatments may be available.

KRAS and NRAS mutations
RAS is a family of genes that includes the HRAS, KRAS, and NRAS genes. Some colon cancers have mutations in the KRAS or NRAS genes. Genes work as instruction manuals for making important proteins. As a result, the proteins these genes make are overactive and can tell the cancer to grow.

BRAF mutation
Fewer than 10 out of 100 colon cancers have a mutation called BRAF V600E. This mutation may cause cancer cells to grow and spread quickly. If your cancer has this mutation, treatments that target abnormal BRAF may be helpful.

HER2 amplification

HER2 is a protein involved in normal cell growth. Having too much HER2 can cause cancer cells to grow and spread quickly. Only about 3 to 5 out of 100 people with colon cancer have too much HER2. HER2 testing is recommended for everyone with metastatic colon cancer unless there is a known *RAS* or *BRAF* mutation. It can help your doctor determine whether systemic therapies that target HER2 may help you.

Fertility and family planning

For unknown reasons, colon cancer is being diagnosed more often in young adults. Some cancer treatments can cause or contribute to infertility. Infertility is the inability to have children. If you want the option of having children after treatment or are unsure, tell your doctors. There are ways for people with cancer to be able to have children after treatment. This is called fertility preservation.

If you are of childbearing age, your doctor will discuss any fertility-related risks of your treatment plan with you. You may be referred for counseling about fertility preservation options. Some of these options are described below.

Sperm banking

Sperm banking stores semen for later use by freezing it in liquid nitrogen. The medical term for this is semen cryopreservation.

Egg freezing

Like sperm banking, unfertilized eggs can be removed, frozen, and stored for later use. The medical term for this is oocyte cryopreservation.

Ovarian tissue banking

This method involves removing part or all of an ovary and freezing the part that contains the eggs. The frozen tissue that contains the eggs can later be unfrozen and put back in the body.

Ovarian transposition

This procedure moves one or both ovaries and fallopian tubes out of the range of the radiation beam. The medical term for this procedure is oophoropexy.

For more information on fertility and family planning, see the *NCCN Guidelines for Patients: Adolescents and Young Adults with Cancer* at NCCN.org/patientguidelines.

Key points

Health history

> Inherited syndromes related to colon cancer include Lynch syndrome and FAP.

> Everyone with colon cancer should be asked about their family health history.

Blood tests

> A complete blood count, chemistry profile, and carcinoembryonic antigen (CEA) test are recommended as part of initial testing.

Imaging

> CT with contrast is the primary imaging test used to determine the extent of colon cancer in the body.

Biomarker testing

> Biomarker testing is used to learn whether your cancer has any targetable changes to help guide your treatment.

> MMR or MSI testing is recommended for everyone diagnosed with colon cancer.

> Testing for *KRAS/NRAS* and *BRAF* mutations is recommended for everyone with metastatic colon cancer.

> HER2 testing is also recommended for everyone with metastatic colon cancer unless there is a known *RAS* or *BRAF* mutation.

Fertility and family planning

> Young adults diagnosed with colon cancer should be counseled about fertility-

related risks of treatment and options for preserving fertility.

We want your feedback!

Our goal is to provide helpful and easy-to-understand information on cancer.

Take our survey to let us know what we got right and what we could do better:

NCCN.org/patients/feedback

3
Overview of treatments

This chapter describes the treatments for colon cancer. If it is an option, surgery is the preferred and most effective treatment. Chemotherapy may be given after surgery, or in place of surgery if the cancer cannot be resected (removed by surgery).

Colon surgery

Another name for surgery that removes tissue, or all or part of an organ, is resection. Cancer that can be removed completely by resection is called resectable.

You may have more than one type of surgery. Surgery to remove liver or lung metastases is described in the "Local therapies for metastases" section on page 28. Your

treatment team will tell you how to prepare for and what to expect during surgery. You may need to stop taking some medicines to reduce the risk of severe bleeding. Eating less, changing to a liquid diet, or using enemas or laxatives will empty your colon for surgery. Right before surgery, you will be given general anesthesia.

Colectomy

A colectomy is a surgery that removes the part of the colon with cancer. After the cancerous part is removed, the two healthy ends of the remaining colon are reconnected. They are either sewn or stapled together.

Lymph nodes near the tumor are also removed during colectomy. Lymph node removal is called lymphadenectomy. At least 12 lymph nodes near the tumor should be removed and

---

Colectomy

Surgery for colon cancer is called colectomy. It involves removing the cancerous part of the colon. The two healthy ends of the remaining colon are then attached to each other.

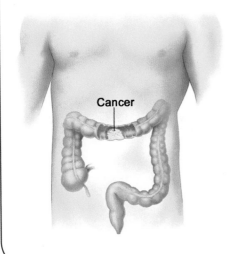
Cancer

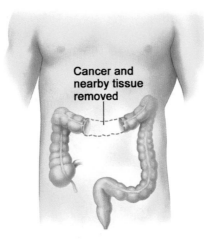
Cancer and nearby tissue removed

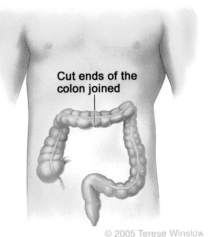
Cut ends of the colon joined

© 2005 Terese Winslow
U.S. Govt. has certain rights

tested for cancer. Any abnormal-looking nodes will also be removed.

A colectomy can be done in two ways. The open method removes cancerous tissue through a large cut in your abdomen. The minimally invasive method involves making a few small cuts. Tools are inserted through the cuts to see and remove part of your colon.

A colectomy can take 1 to 4 hours to complete. You may stay in the hospital for several days to recover. After surgery, you will be told what you can and cannot eat to prevent discomfort and help healing.

Colostomy

At the time of colectomy, some people may also have a procedure called a colostomy. This is done in cases where it may not be safe to reconnect the remaining sections of colon.

In a colostomy, the remaining upper part of the colon is attached to an opening on the surface of the abdomen. This opening is called a stoma. Stool exits the body through the stoma and goes into a bag attached to the skin. This is typically only needed for a short time. For colon cancer surgery, it is rare for a colostomy not to be reversed with another operation. Colostomy is also known as diversion because it diverts (redirects) the flow of stool.

Colostomy

If the two healthy ends of the remaining colon cannot be safely reconnected after the cancer is removed, a colostomy may be performed. A colostomy connects a part of the colon to the outside of the abdomen. This creates an opening in your abdomen that allows stool to pass through. For colon cancer surgery, it is rare for a colostomy not to be reversed with another operation.

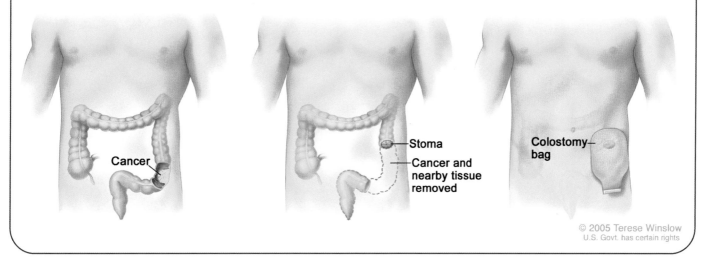

© 2005 Terese Winslow
U.S. Govt. has certain rights

Side effects of surgery

Surgery causes pain, swelling, and scars. Pain and swelling often fade away in the weeks following surgery. Scars from surgery do not go away completely. As with any surgery, there is also a chance of complications. These include major blood loss, infection, heart attack, and blood clots. There can also be injury to nearby organs. Your surgical team will design care to try to prevent these risks.

There are short- and long-term side effects specific to colectomy. In the days or weeks following colon resection, food, digested debris, or stool may leak out where the colon was reconnected. This is known as anastomotic leak. It can cause pain, fever, and life-threatening infection.

Colectomy can also cause a change in bowel habits. You may experience changes in the frequency or urgency of your bowel movements.

It is common for scar tissue to form after abdominal surgery. In some cases, however, there is so much scar tissue that the bowel becomes obstructed (blocked). In rare cases, the bowel may become tightly wrapped around an area of scar tissue. This is an emergency that requires surgery.

A possible long-term effect of colon surgery is hernia. Hernia refers to organs pushing through tissues or muscles weakened by surgery.

Not all complications and side effects of surgery are listed here. Ask your treatment team for a complete list of common and rare side effects.

Systemic therapy

Systemic therapy is the use of medicine to kill cancer cells. The medicine(s) travel in the bloodstream to reach cells throughout the body. Systemic therapy can kill healthy cells in addition to cancer cells. The damage to healthy cells can cause harsh side effects, such as hair loss, cracked skin, and mouth sores. Most commonly, systemic therapy is given intravenously. This means the medicine is slowly infused into the bloodstream through a vein.

Types of systemic therapy include chemotherapy, targeted therapy, and immunotherapy. If systemic therapy is planned, the regimen(s) given depends (in part) on:

> Whether the cancer has spread beyond the colon

> Whether surgery is possible or planned

> Whether the cancer has any biomarkers (see page 20 for more information)

> Your general health

General information on the main types of systemic therapy is provided next. Specific recommendations for the use of systemic therapy are provided later in this guide.

If systemic therapy is planned, ask your treatment team for a full list of common and rare side effects of each drug you are receiving.

Chemotherapy

Chemotherapy is given in cycles of treatment days followed by days of rest. This allows your body to recover between cycles. Cycles vary in length depending on which drugs are used.

Chemotherapy regimens often used to treat colon cancer are listed in Guide 1.

The side effects of chemotherapy depend on many things (drug type, dosage, length of treatment) and are different for everyone. Common side effects include nausea, loss of appetite, diarrhea, hair loss, and mouth sores.

Some regimens are considered "intensive." This means they may be harsh on the body. FOLFOX, CAPEOX, FOLFIRI, and FOLFIRINOX are intensive regimens. Any chemotherapy regimen that has "OX" in the name means the regimen includes oxaliplatin. Oxaliplatin can cause nerve damage to your fingers and toes. Symptoms include numbness, cramping, tingling, or pain in these areas.

Any chemotherapy regimen that has "IRI" in the name means it contains irinotecan. Irinotecan tends to cause abdominal cramping, nausea, diarrhea, and hair loss. It does not have the effects on nerves seen with oxaliplatin.

If regimens containing oxaliplatin and/or irinotecan are expected to be too harsh, your doctor may recommend 5-fluorouracil (5-FU)/ leucovorin or capecitabine alone. However, these regimens can also cause potentially harsh side effects. Capecitabine can cause a side effect known as hand-foot syndrome. Symptoms include redness, swelling, and pain on the palms of the hands, bottoms of feet, or both. Sometimes blisters appear. Your dose of capecitabine may be changed at the earliest signs of hand-foot syndrome.

Targeted therapy and immunotherapy

Unlike chemotherapy, targeted therapy and immunotherapy are most effective at treating cancers with specific features, called biomarkers. These newer types of systemic therapy may be treatment options for patients with advanced colon cancer.

Targeted therapies can target and attack specific receptors found on cancer cells. One type stops the growth of new blood vessels into colon tumors. Without the blood they need to grow, cancer cells "starve" and die. A second type stops the cancer cells from

Guide 1
Combination chemotherapy regimens

FOLFOX	**FOL** = Leucovorin calcium **F** = Fluorouracil **OX** = Oxaliplatin
CAPEOX	**CAPE** = Capecitabine **OX** = Oxaliplatin
FOLFIRI	**FOL** = Leucovorin calcium **F** = Fluorouracil **IRI** = Irinotecan
FOLFIRINOX	**FOL** = Leucovorin calcium **F** = Fluorouracil **IRI** = Irinotecan **OX** = Oxaliplatin
5-FU/LV	**FU** = Fluorouracil **LV** = Leucovorin calcium

receiving signals to grow. Other types work in more than one way. A targeted therapy known as a biologic may be added to chemotherapy to treat advanced colon cancer.

The immune system is your body's natural defense against infection and disease. Immunotherapy increases the activity of your immune system, improving your body's ability to find and destroy cancer cells. Immune checkpoint inhibitors are a type of immunotherapy used to treat colon cancer.

For more information on the side effects of immune checkpoint inhibitors, see the *NCCN Guidelines for Patients: Immunotherapy Side Effects: Immune Checkpoint Inhibitors* at NCCN.org/patientguidelines.

Local therapies for metastases

Treatment options for metastatic colon cancer may include local therapies. Local therapies are treatments that target metastatic tumors directly. Some may be used in place of or in addition to surgery.

Several of the local therapies described next are performed by an interventional oncologist/radiologist. Interventional oncology/radiology is a medical specialty that uses imaging techniques to deliver minimally invasive cancer treatments. Computed tomography (CT), ultrasound, magnetic resonance imaging (MRI), and positron emission tomography (PET)/CT are imaging techniques that may be used. The use of imaging during the procedure allows the doctor to precisely target the tumor(s). Interventional oncology/radiology treatments are also known as image-guided therapies.

Resection

Surgery, also called resection, is often the preferred way to remove colon cancer that has spread to the liver or lungs. Resection removes the cancerous part of the liver or lung(s). Another name for surgery to remove a metastasis is metastasectomy.

If the metastatic tumors are small, image-guided ablation (described on the next page), may be offered instead of surgery in some cases. It may have similar results, but with fewer complications and a shorter recovery time.

If resection is possible but is not expected to completely remove the metastases, combined treatment with both surgery and ablation may be an option.

Resection may not be possible because you have risk factors or certain health conditions. In this case, ablation or other local therapies described on the next pages may be an option for treating metastases.

A team of experts can determine the best local therapy for your metastatic tumor(s).

Portal vein embolization
If your doctor thinks your liver will be too small after a liver resection, you may need to have it enlarged. This is done using a minimally invasive procedure called portal vein embolization (PVE). An interventional radiologist uses a catheter inserted into certain veins in the liver. This blocks the blood vessel to the liver tumor, causing the healthy part of the liver to grow larger.

Image-guided ablation
Image-guided ablation destroys small liver or lung tumors with little harm to nearby tissue. It may be performed by either an interventional radiologist or a surgeon. Ablation may be used in addition to surgery. Or, it may be used by itself for small tumors that can be completely destroyed. Ablation will only be used if all visible areas of cancer can be destroyed. In some cases, ablation can be done as an outpatient in the interventional radiology department in a single session.

At this time, the most commonly used ablative therapies are radiofrequency (RFA) and microwave ablation. These methods kill cancer cells using heat. The delivery of cold energy (cryoablation) is also used, mostly for lung tumors. Less common ablative methods include irreversible electroporation, also known as "nanoknife," and laser ablation.

All ablative therapies are delivered using a specialized needle called a "probe" or "electrode" placed directly into or next to the target tumor. All types of ablation kill cancer cells by delivering targeted energy into the tumor while sparing or minimizing damage to normal tissues.

Liver-directed therapies
If the cancer has spread only (or mainly) to the liver, treatment with intra-arterial liver-directed therapies may be an option. This type of local therapy will be considered for liver tumors that:

> Did not (or no longer) improve with chemotherapy, and

> Cannot be resected or ablated.

Intra-arterial therapies treat liver tumors with chemotherapy beads (chemoembolization) or radioactive spheres (radioembolization). If radiation spheres are used, it is known as selective internal radiation therapy (SIRT) or transarterial hepatic radioembolization (TARE). These procedures are performed by interventional oncologists/radiologists.

A catheter is inserted into an artery in your leg or wrist and guided to the liver tumor(s). Once in place, the spheres or beads are injected into the blood vessel leading to the tumor. The spheres or beads collect inside the tumor and deliver radiation or chemotherapy, causing the cancer cells to die. The chemotherapy beads can also work to stop the blood supply to the tumor and starve the tumor. The chemotherapy or radiation further damage the cancer cells and cause the tumor to shrink. When embolization with chemotherapy is not an option, bland embolization with small beads may be used. This involves physically blocking the blood supply to the tumor.

Another intra-arterial liver-directed therapy is hepatic arterial infusion chemotherapy (HAIC). While chemotherapy is traditionally given intravenously to reach cells throughout the body, HAIC is given directly to the liver to treat metastases. HAIC is often given in addition to standard intravenous chemotherapy. Using a port or pump that is usually placed during during surgery to remove liver tumors, the drugs are funneled directly into the artery leading to the liver. HAIC should only be performed by medical oncologists at treatment centers with extensive experience in this method.

Radiation therapy

Radiation therapy uses high-energy rays to kill cancer cells. While it is most often used to treat tumors in the liver and/or lungs, it may also be used with chemotherapy to treat cancer in the colon that cannot be removed with surgery.

The type of radiation therapy used most often to treat metastatic colon cancer is **stereotactic body radiation therapy (SBRT)**. SBRT is a highly specialized type of external beam radiation therapy (EBRT). External means that the radiation beams come from a large machine outside the body. The radiation passes through skin and other tissue to reach the tumor.

In SBRT, treatment is typically delivered in 5 or fewer sessions, called fractions. High doses of radiation are delivered to a metastatic

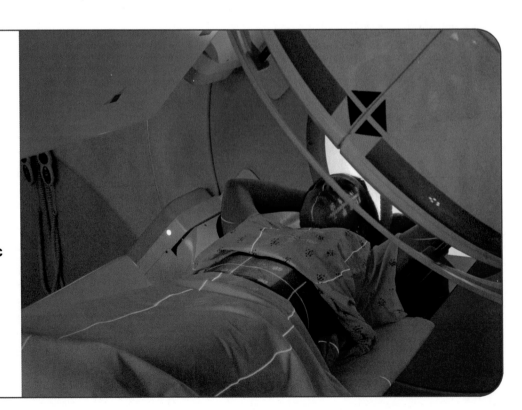

Stereotactic body radiation therapy (SBRT)

SBRT may be used to treat colon cancer that has spread to the liver, lungs, or bone. High doses of radiation are delivered to a metastatic site or sites using very precise beams. Treatment is typically given in 5 or fewer sessions.

site or sites using very precise beams. The treatment setup for SBRT is often more complex than typical external radiation therapy. This is because higher doses of radiation are delivered. SBRT may be used to treat colon cancer that has spread to the liver, lungs, or bone.

Other types of EBRT include three-dimensional conformal radiation therapy (3D-CRT) and intensity-modulated radiation therapy (IMRT). All types are conformal, which means that the radiation beams are shaped to the cancer site. This helps minimize damage to healthy tissue. The type used depends on the location and size of the tumor(s) and other factors.

If radiation therapy is planned

A planning session is needed before treatment begins. This is called simulation. After being guided into the treatment position, pictures of the cancer sites are made with an imaging test. Using the pictures, the radiation team plans the best radiation dose and number of treatments.

During treatment, you will lie on a table as you did for simulation. Devices may be used to keep you from moving. This helps to target the tumor. Radiation beams are aimed with help from ink marks on your skin or marker seeds in the tumor.

You will be alone in the treatment room. A technician will operate the machine from a nearby room and will be able to see, hear, and speak with you at all times. As treatment is given, you may hear noises. You will not see, hear, or feel the radiation. One session can take less than 10 minutes.

Side effects of radiation therapy include:

> Feeling tired and worn out

> Hair loss in the treated area

> Changes to urination and bowel movements

> Diarrhea

> Nausea and vomiting

Late side effects can include infertility, lung scarring, heart disease, and second cancers. Not all side effects are listed here. Ask your treatment team for a full list.

Clinical trials

A clinical trial is a type of medical research study. After being developed and tested in a laboratory, potential new ways of fighting cancer need to be studied in people. If found to be safe and effective in a clinical trial, a drug, device, or treatment approach may be approved by the U.S. Food and Drug Administration (FDA).

Everyone with cancer should carefully consider all of the treatment options available for their cancer type, including standard treatments and clinical trials. Talk to your doctor about whether a clinical trial may make sense for you.

Phases

Most cancer clinical trials focus on treatment. Treatment trials are done in phases.

> **Phase I** trials study the safety and side effects of an investigational drug or treatment approach.

> **Phase II** trials study how well the drug or approach works against a specific type of cancer.

> **Phase III** trials test the drug or approach against a standard treatment. If the results are good, it may be approved by the FDA.

> **Phase IV** trials study the long-term safety and benefit of an FDA-approved treatment.

Who can enroll?

Every clinical trial has rules for joining, called eligibility criteria. The rules may be about age, cancer type and stage, treatment history, or general health. These requirements ensure

Finding a clinical trial

In the United States

NCCN Cancer Centers
NCCN.org/cancercenters

The National Cancer Institute (NCI)
cancer.gov/about-cancer/treatment/
clinical-trials/search

Worldwide

The U.S. National Library of Medicine (NLM)
clinicaltrials.gov

Need help finding a clinical trial?
NCI's Cancer Information Service (CIS)
1.800.4.CANCER (1.800.422.6237)
cancer.gov/contact

that participants are alike in specific ways and that the trial is as safe as possible for the participants.

Informed consent

Clinical trials are managed by a group of experts called a research team. The research team will review the study with you in detail, including its purpose and the risks and benefits of joining. All of this information is also provided in an informed consent form. Read the form carefully and ask questions before signing it. Take time to discuss with family, friends, or others you trust. Keep in mind that you can leave and seek treatment outside of the clinical trial at any time.

Start the conversation

Don't wait for your doctor to bring up clinical trials. Start the conversation and learn about all of your treatment options. If you find a study that you may be eligible for, ask your treatment team if you meet the requirements. Try not to be discouraged if you cannot join. New clinical trials are always becoming available.

Frequently asked questions

There are many myths and misconceptions surrounding clinical trials. The possible benefits and risks are not well understood by many with cancer.

Will I get a placebo?

Placebos (inactive versions of real medicines) are almost never used alone in cancer clinical trials. It is common to receive either a placebo with a standard treatment, or a new drug with a standard treatment. You will be informed, verbally and in writing, if a placebo is part of a clinical trial before you enroll.

Are clinical trials free?

There is no fee to enroll in a clinical trial. The study sponsor pays for research-related costs, including the study drug. You may, however, have costs indirectly related to the trial, such as the cost of transportation or child care due to extra appointments. During the trial, you will continue to receive standard cancer care.

This care is billed to—and often covered by—insurance. You are responsible for copays and any costs for this care that are not covered by your insurance.

Key points

Colon surgery

> A colectomy is surgery that removes part of the colon. Nearby lymph nodes are also removed and tested for cancer.

> If the remaining ends of the colon cannot be safely reconnected during colectomy, a colostomy may be performed.

> A colostomy involves attaching the remaining upper part of the colon to an opening (stoma) on the abdomen. It is usually temporary.

Systemic therapy

> Systemic therapy is the use of medicine to kill cancer cells throughout the body.

> Types of systemic therapy include chemotherapy, targeted therapy, and immunotherapy.

> Chemotherapy regimens often used to treat colon cancer include FOLFOX, CAPEOX, FOLFIRI, FOLFIRINOX, and 5-FU/LV.

Local therapies for metastases

> Local therapies are treatments that target metastatic tumors directly. Some may be used in place of or in addition to surgery.

> Local therapies include resection, image-guided ablation, stereotactic body radiation therapy (SBRT), and intra-arterial liver-directed therapies.

Clinical trials

> Clinical trials give people access to investigational treatments that may, in time, be approved by the U.S. Food and Drug Administration (FDA).

4
Non-metastatic colon cancer

This chapter explains treatment for colon cancer that has not spread to areas far from the colon.

Colon cancer often forms in polyps on the lining of the colon. It can also take the form of lesions on the inside of the colon.

Cancerous polyps

A polyp is an overgrowth of cells on the inner lining of the colon wall. The most common type is called an adenoma. Adenomas are considered pre-cancerous. While it may take many years, adenomas can become invasive colon cancer. Cancer that forms in an adenoma is known as an adenocarcinoma.

The two main shapes of polyps are sessile and pedunculated. Pedunculated polyps are shaped like mushrooms and stick out from the colon wall. They have a stalk and round top. Sessile polyps are flatter and do not have a stalk.

A polyp in which cancer has just started to grow is called a malignant (cancerous) polyp. Most polyps can be removed during a

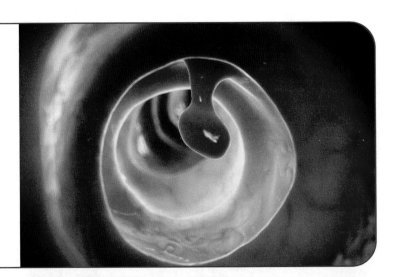

Pedunculated polyp

Pedunculated polyps have a stalk and are mushroom-like in appearance.

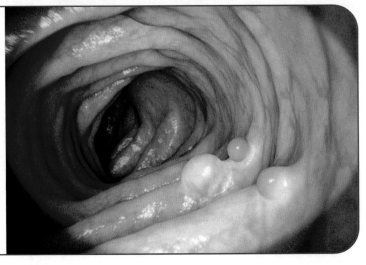

Sessile polyp

Sessile polyps do not have a stalk and lie flatter against the lining of the colon wall.

colonoscopy, using a minor surgical procedure called a polypectomy. In some cases, no further treatment is needed after a polypectomy.

In other cases, surgery (resection) of a bigger piece of the colon is needed. This depends on:

> The size and shape of the polyp (pedunculated or sessile),

> The polypectomy results, and

> The results of testing the removed tissue.

Before deciding whether resection is needed after a polypectomy, your doctor will review the results of testing with you and discuss your options.

Good polypectomy results
No further treatment is needed for a cancerous **pedunculated** polyp that was fully removed in one piece and found to be low-risk based on testing.

Cancerous **sessile** polyps, however, are more likely to return after polypectomy. They also tend to have other poor treatment outcomes. For this reason, colectomy (surgery) is a recommended treatment option for sessile polyps—even those with good results of polypectomy and testing. See page 24 for information on colectomy. Observation is also an option for sessile polyps. If surgery is planned, see "Chemotherapy after surgery" on page 39 for next steps.

Other polypectomy results
If the polyp is not removed in one piece, or testing of the removed polyp finds high-risk features, surgery may be needed. If high-risk features are found, more tests to determine the extent of the cancer are recommended. This includes blood tests and a computed tomography (CT) scan of the chest, abdomen, and pelvis. If testing finds that surgery is needed, surgery (colectomy) is recommended. Chemotherapy may be given after surgery. See "Chemotherapy after surgery" on page 39 for next steps.

If surgery is needed

If the cancer is not found early enough to be removed by polypectomy, surgery (colectomy) is needed. Surgery is only an option if the colon tumor can be completely removed. If you are not a candidate for surgery, see page 40.

The true extent of the cancer cannot be known until after surgery. It can be estimated, however, based on the results of testing. Testing before surgery includes:

> Colonoscopy

> Biopsy and testing of removed tissue

> Mismatch repair (MMR) or microsatellite instability (MSI) testing

> Blood tests including complete blood count (CBC), chemistry profile, and carcinoembryonic antigen (CEA) level

> CT scan of the chest, abdomen, and pelvis with contrast

> Additional imaging tests as needed

More information on these tests can be found in *Part 2: Treatment planning* on page 14.

In some cases, chemotherapy or immunotherapy is given before surgery. The goal is to shrink the colon tumor so it can be fully removed during surgery. Systemic therapy may be given before surgery if:

> The tumor has grown through the colon wall and invaded nearby structures

> There are many or very large lymph nodes suspected to be cancerous.

Chemotherapy regimens commonly used before surgery include FOLFOX and CAPEOX. If the tumor is MMR deficient or MSI-high (dMMR/MSI-H), immunotherapy with one of the following may be an option:

> Nivolumab (Opdivo) with or without ipilimumab (Yervoy)

> Pembrolizumab (Keytruda)

The tissue removed during surgery is sent to a pathologist. The pathologist assesses how far the cancer has grown within the colon wall and tests the removed lymph nodes for cancer. Based on the results of testing, the cancer stage is assigned. The stage helps determine whether chemotherapy is needed after surgery. See "Chemotherapy after surgery" on the next page.

If the bowel is blocked

In rare cases, a tumor may grow so large that it blocks the flow of stool. There are several ways to deal with a blockage. One option is a colectomy that also unblocks the bowel. This is known as a one-stage colectomy.

Another option is colectomy with colostomy. In a colostomy, the remaining upper part of the colon is attached to an opening on the surface of the abdomen. This opening is called a stoma. Stool exits the body through the stoma and goes into a bag attached to the skin. This is typically only needed for a short time. Colostomy is also known as diversion because it diverts (redirects) the flow of stool. See page 25 for an illustration of colostomy.

Another possibility is that a colostomy may be done first, followed by a second surgery to remove the cancer. Lastly, a mesh metal tube called a stent may be placed first, followed by a second surgery to remove the cancer. The stent keeps the colon open, allowing gas and stool to pass.

Chemotherapy after surgery

Chemotherapy may be given after surgery. The goal is to kill cancer cells that may remain in the body. Decisions about chemotherapy are guided in large part by the cancer stage.

Stage I

Observation (no chemotherapy) is recommended after surgery for all stage I colon cancers.

Stage II

Observation is recommended after surgery for most low-risk stage II cancers, especially MSI-H/dMMR tumors. Whether chemotherapy is needed after surgery is less clear for stage II cancers that **are not** MSI-H/dMMR. These are called microsatellite stable (MSS) or mismatch repair proficient (pMMR) tumors. MSS/pMMR cancers can be observed or treated with chemotherapy. To help guide decision-making, your doctor will consider the risk of the cancer returning after treatment (recurrence). This risk is based on findings during surgery and analysis of the removed tissue.

If chemotherapy is planned, recommended regimens for both high-and low-risk stage II colon cancer include capecitabine and 5-fluorouracil (5-FU)/leucovorin. FOLFOX and CAPEOX are recommended options for high-risk disease. See Guide 2.

Stage III

Chemotherapy is recommended after surgery for all stage III colon cancers. Recommended regimens include CAPEOX, FOLFOX, capecitabine, and 5-FU. Chemotherapy after surgery is typically given for 3 to 6 months. The length of treatment depends on the regimen and the risk of recurrence. See Guide 2.

Guide 2 — Treatment after surgery for stage II and III cancers		
Stage II	**MSI-H/dMMR**	Observation (no chemotherapy)
	MSS/pMMR	Observation OR chemotherapy with one of the following: • Capecitabine (6 months) (for low or high risk of recurrence) • 5-FU/leucovorin (6 months) (for low or high risk of recurrence) • FOLFOX (6 months) (only for high risk of recurrence) • CAPEOX (3 months) (only for high risk of recurrence)
Stage III		Chemotherapy with one of the following: • CAPEOX (3 months if low risk of recurrence; 3–6 months if high risk of recurrence) • FOLFOX (3–6 months if low risk of recurrence; 6 months if high risk of recurrence) • Capecitabine (6 months) • 5-FU (6 months)

If surgery is not an option

Surgery may not be possible because of the location of the tumor or because of other health issues. In this case, treatment options include systemic therapy and chemoradiation. Chemoradiation involves treatment with both chemotherapy and radiation therapy.

If systemic therapy is planned, there are a number of possible regimens that may be used. The choice of regimen depends on whether the tumor has any biomarkers and how well you are expected to tolerate certain systemic therapies. See page 20 for more information on biomarkers.

If chemoradiation is planned, chemotherapy medicines recommended for use with radiation include 5-FU and capecitabine. 5-FU is given by infusion; capecitabine is taken by mouth. If you are unable to tolerate either of these, a third option for use with radiation is bolus 5-FU/leucovorin. Bolus refers to the use of a single dose given over a short period of time.

After treatment with systemic therapy or chemoradiation, the size of the tumor will be checked to see if it is resectable (able to be removed with surgery). If the tumor does not become resectable, systemic therapy is continued.

If the tumor becomes resectable, surgery is recommended. After surgery, chemotherapy is recommended to kill any remaining cancer cells. Currently recommended regimens for use after surgery include FOLFOX, CAPEOX, capecitabine, and 5-FU/leucovorin. After chemotherapy, surveillance begins.

Let us know what you think!

Please take a moment to complete an online survey about the NCCN Guidelines for Patients.

NCCN.org/patients/response

Surveillance

Follow-up testing is started when there are no signs of cancer after treatment. It is helpful for finding new cancer growth early.

Stage I

A colonoscopy is recommended 1 year after surgery for stage I colon cancer. If results are normal, the next colonoscopy should be in 3 years, and then every 5 years. If an advanced adenoma is found, your next colonoscopy will be needed within 1 year. Advanced adenomas include polyps with a ruffled structure (villous), a polyp larger than 1 cm, or a polyp with pre-cancerous cells (high-grade dysplasia).

If you don't have any symptoms, other testing is not needed on a regular basis. Imaging tests may be ordered if your doctor thinks the cancer may have come back or spread.

Stages II and III

In addition to colonoscopy, surveillance for stages II and III colon cancer includes physical exams, CEA blood tests, and CT scans. Rising CEA levels may be a sign that colon cancer has returned. CT scans can find metastases, should any develop. The recommended schedule for surveillance testing is shown in Guide 3.

In addition to surveillance testing, a range of other care is important for cancer survivors. See *Part 6: Survivorship* on page 53 for more information.

Guide 3 Surveillance for stage II and stage III colon cancer	
Medical history and physical exam	Every 3–6 months for first 2 years, then every 6 months for 3 more years
CEA blood test	Every 3–6 months for first 2 years, then every 6 months for 3 more years
CT of chest, abdomen, and pelvis	Every 6–12 months for 5 years
Colonoscopy	**No total colonoscopy at diagnosis:** 3 to 6 months after surgery **Total colonoscopy at diagnosis:** 1 year after surgery If no advanced adenoma, repeat in 3 years, then every 5 years If advanced adenoma, repeat in 1 year

Key points

Cancerous polyps

> No further treatment is needed for a malignant pedunculated polyp that was removed in one piece and found to be low risk based on testing.

> Malignant sessile polyps are more likely to return after polypectomy than pedunculated polyps. Surgery and observation are options for sessile polyps.

If surgery is needed

> Colectomy is needed for cancer that is not found early enough to be removed by polypectomy. If surgery is not possible, systemic therapy and chemoradiation are options.

> Chemotherapy or immunotherapy may be given before surgery for a tumor that has invaded nearby organs or structures, or if there are many lymph nodes with cancer.

> Observation is recommended after surgery for all stage I cancers and most low-risk stage II cancers, especiallly MSI-H/dMMR tumors.

> After surgery, stage II cancers that are not MSI-H/dMMR can be observed or treated with chemotherapy. The risk of recurrence based on the results of surgery and testing will be considered.

> Chemotherapy is recommended after surgery for all stage III colon cancers.

Surveillance

> Colonoscopies are used to monitor for the return of stage I colon cancer. Your doctor may also recommend physical exams and CEA blood tests.

> Surveillance for stages II and III colon cancer includes physical exams, CEA blood tests, colonoscopies, and CT scans.

5
Metastatic colon cancer

Colon cancer spreads most often to the liver, sometimes to the lungs, and less often to the abdomen or other areas. Cancer may have already spread by the time it is diagnosed. This is stage IV colon cancer. More commonly, metastases develop after treatment for non-metastatic colon cancer.

About half of people with colon cancer will develop metastases. Most will be liver metastases that cannot be removed with surgery. This section covers both stage IV colon cancer and metastasis after treatment. Although both are considered metastatic cancer, there are some differences in treatment.

Stage IV colon cancer

If there is cancer in areas far from the colon when you are first diagnosed, the cancer is stage IV. Testing for suspected (or known) stage IV colon cancer includes:

> Biopsy

> Colonoscopy

> Computed tomography (CT) of the chest, abdomen, and pelvis

> Other imaging as needed to help determine if you can have surgery

> Blood tests including complete blood count (CBC), chemistry profile, and carcinoembryonic antigen (CEA) level

> Biomarker testing

The presence of biomarkers helps guide treatment for metastatic colon cancer. Everyone with metastatic colon cancer should have their tumor tested for the biomarkers listed below.

> *RAS* and *BRAF* mutations

> HER2 amplification (not needed if there is a *RAS* or *BRAF* mutation)

> Mismatch repair deficiency (dMMR)/ microsatellite instability-high (MSI-H) (if not already performed)

Testing for these biomarkers may be performed individually, or as part of a larger panel (group). Testing for many biomarkers at one time is called next-generation sequencing (NGS). NGS can find other, rare gene mutations for which targeted treatments may be available.

See *Part 2: Treatment planning* for more information on recommended testing.

Cancer in the liver and/or lungs

When possible, surgery (resection) is the preferred way to treat colon cancer that has spread to the liver or lungs. In some patients with small tumors, image-guided ablation may be offered instead of surgery. It may have similar results but fewer complications.

When surgery is not expected to completely remove the metastases, combination treatment with ablation may be an option. For patients unable to undergo resection due to other health conditions, treatment with ablation or other local therapies may be possible. See page 28 for information on local therapies for metastases.

To learn if surgery or treatment with local therapies is an option, your case should be evaluated by a multidisciplinary team of experts. The team should include a surgeon experienced in removing liver and lung tumors and an interventional oncologist/radiologist with expertise in image-guided therapies such as ablation or hepatic arterial liver-directed therapies. If you can have surgery first, see "Upfront surgery is possible" on page 46.

If liver and lung tumors cannot be removed with surgery and/or ablation, radiation therapy may be considered. If treatment with these local therapies is not possible, stage IV colon cancer is treated with systemic therapy. Systemic therapy given first is called first-line therapy.

First-line systemic therapy

One of the following chemotherapy regimens is usually given first:

> FOLFIRI

> FOLFOX

> CAPEOX

> FOLFIRINOX

A targeted therapy known as a biologic may also be included in the regimen. Biologics include:

> Bevacizumab (Avastin)

> Panitumumab (Vectibix)

> Cetuximab (Erbitux)

Panitumumab and cetuximab are only used for tumors in the left side of the colon that have normal *RAS* and *BRAF* genes.

For MSI-H or dMMR tumors, immunotherapy may also be an option for first-line therapy. There is less research available on this option. If your cancer has this biomarker, talk to your doctor about immunotherapy versus chemotherapy. Immunotherapies recommended at this time include pembrolizumab (Keytruda) and nivolumab (Opdivo). Nivolumab may be given with another immunotherapy called ipilimumab (Yervoy).

Although uncommon, systemic therapy may shrink the tumors enough to be removed with surgery and/or local therapies. If this occurs, surgery is recommended. The colon tumor and the metastases may be removed during the same procedure or in 2 separate surgeries. After surgery, most people will have more systemic therapy. In some cases, observation or a short course of chemotherapy may be possible. After any systemic therapy given after surgery, surveillance begins. See page 49.

If the tumors do not become resectable during first-line therapy, systemic therapy is typically continued. The goal is to slow the growth and spread of the cancer. In select cases treatment with local therapies may be possible. If one systemic therapy regimen does not work or stops working, there are other options. These are called second- and third-line regimens. Some of the options depend on what treatment you've already had. See the next page for more information.

Second-line therapy and beyond

If the cancer progresses, the regimen you receive for second-line therapy may be different from what you had before. The choice of regimen will depend on:

> prior systemic therapy received

> how well you are expected to tolerate certain systemic therapies

> whether the tumor has any biomarkers.

Options for MSI-H or dMMR tumors may include:

> Pembrolizumab (Keytruda)

> Nivolumab (Opdivo) with or without ipilimumab (Yervoy)

> Dostarlimab-gxly (Jemperli)

Options for HER2-positive cancers include:

> Trastuzumab (Herceptin) with either pertuzumab (Perjeta) or lapatinib (Tykerb)

> Fam-trastuzumab deruxtecan-nxki (Enhertu)

If the cancer progresses again, third-line systemic therapy options may include:

> Chemotherapy with trifluridine and tipiracil (Lonsurf)

> Targeted therapy with regorafenib (Stivarga)

Both are tablets taken by mouth. The targeted therapy bevacizumab may be given with Lonsurf.

Upfront surgery is possible

If all areas of cancer can be completely removed using surgery and/or other local therapies, this is recommended for stage IV colon cancer. All of the options that include surgery also involve systemic therapy. Chemotherapy regimens often used are listed below. The choice of regimen depends on whether chemotherapy is given before or after surgery and other factors.

> FOLFOX

> CAPEOX

> FOLFIRI

> FOLFIRINOX

> Capecitabine

> 5-FU/leucovorin

The treatment options are described next and listed in Guide 4 on the next page.

Option 1: This option starts with surgery to remove the colon tumor and the liver or lung tumors. The surgeries may be done at the same time or in two procedures. While surgery is preferred to remove the metastases, other local therapies may be helpful if there are only a few small metastases. Local therapies include ablation and stereotactic body radiation therapy (SBRT).

The next phase of this treatment option is chemotherapy. The goal is to kill any cancer cells that may remain in the body. After chemotherapy, surveillance begins.

Option 2: This option starts with chemotherapy. Benefits of chemotherapy before surgery can include:

> You may receive early treatment of possible cancer not yet found

> Knowing your response to chemotherapy early can help with treatment planning

> If the cancer grows during chemotherapy, you can avoid local treatment

Disadvantages of chemotherapy before surgery can include:

> The cancer does not respond to treatment and grows

> The cancer responds to treatment but shrinks so much that it is undetectable, and therefore cannot be removed with surgery

> Surgery can no longer be performed because of liver injury caused by side effects

After 2 to 3 months of chemotherapy, the next step is surgery and/or treatment with local therapies. The colon tumor and the metastases may be removed in one surgery or in two separate surgeries. The next phase of this treatment option is more chemotherapy. After chemotherapy, surveillance begins.

Option 3: This option starts with surgery to remove the colon tumor (colectomy), followed by 2 to 3 months of chemotherapy. Removing the metastases with surgery and/ or local therapies follows chemotherapy. The next phase of this treatment option is more chemotherapy. After chemotherapy, surveillance begins.

Guide 4
Treatment options involving surgery for stage IV colon cancer

Option 1	Surgery and/or local therapy ➡ Chemotherapy
Option 2	Chemotherapy ➡ Surgery ➡ Chemotherapy
Option 3	Colon surgery ➡ Chemotherapy ➡ Metastasectomy ➡ Chemotherapy
Option 4	Immunotherapy ➡ Surgery **Note:** This option is only for dMMR/MSI-H tumors

Option 4: For MSI-H/dMMR tumors, your treatment options may include immunotherapy (instead of chemotherapy) before surgery. There is not as much research available on this option. If your cancer is MSI-H or dMMR, talk to your doctor about immunotherapy versus chemotherapy before surgery. Following immunotherapy, the colon tumor and metastases are removed, either at the same time or in separate surgeries. Local therapies may also be used to destroy metastases. After chemotherapy, surveillance begins.

Cancer in the abdomen

About 17 out of 100 people with metastatic colon cancer will also form tumors in the peritoneum. The peritoneum is the thin layer of tissue that lines the abdomen and covers most of the abdominal organs. The goal of treatment in most cases is to relieve or prevent symptoms. The main treatment is systemic therapy.

Tumors growing in or around the bowel can cause a blockage. If the bowel is blocked, stool cannot move and leave the body. If the cancer is not blocking the bowel, systemic therapy is recommended. The regimen you receive will depend on whether the tumor has any biomarkers and how well you are expected to tolerate certain systemic therapies.

If the cancer is (or is expected to) block the bowel, you will need care to unblock the bowel before starting systemic therapy. This can be done using one of several surgical techniques, or with a mesh metal tube called a stent.

Cytoreductive surgery and HIPEC

Colon cancer that spreads to the abdominal cavity can be difficult to treat. In some cases, cytoreductive surgery and/or hyperthermic intraperitoneal chemotherapy (HIPEC) may be treatment options.

Cytoreductive surgery involves surgically removing all visible tumors. If the tumor cannot be separated from the surface of an organ, the organ may also need to be removed. In HIPEC, a heated chemotherapy solution is put directly into the abdominal cavity through small tubes called catheters. The chemotherapy solution kills remaining microscopic cancer cells without killing healthy cells.

Research is needed on whether the benefits of cytoreductive surgery and HIPEC outweigh the potential harms. The use of HIPEC in particular is very controversial. NCCN experts recommend that these methods only be considered for patients with minimal metastases that can be completely removed with surgery. These procedures should only be carried out at cancer centers experienced in these methods.

Surveillance

Surveillance for stage IV colon cancer includes:

> Colonoscopies

> Physical exams

> CEA blood tests

> CT scans

Rising CEA levels may be a sign that colon cancer has returned. CT scans can help find new metastases. The recommended schedule for surveillance testing is shown in Guide 5.

In addition to surveillance testing, a range of other care is important for cancer survivors. See *Part 6: Survivorship* for more information.

Guide 5
Surveillance for stage IV colon cancer

Medical history and physical exam	Every 3–6 months for first 2 years, then every 6 months for 3 more years
CEA blood test	Every 3–6 months for first 2 years, then every 6 months for 3 more years
CT of chest, abdomen, and pelvis	Every 3–6 months for first 2 years, then every 6–12 months for 3 more years
Colonoscopy	**You did not have a total colonoscopy at diagnosis:** Colonoscopy recommended 3 to 6 months after surgery **You had a total colonoscopy at diagnosis:** Colonoscopy recommended 1 year after surgery • If no advanced adenoma, repeat in 3 years, then every 5 years • If advanced adenoma, repeat in 1 year

Metastasis at recurrence

Cancer may return after initial treatment of non-metastatic disease and spread to the liver, lungs, or other areas. This is called a distant recurrence. Treatment with surgery and/or local therapies is recommended if all of the tumors can be totally removed. However, this is uncommon. You may have a PET/CT scan to help determine whether surgery is possible.

Systemic therapy

Like stage IV colon cancer, distant recurrences are usually treated with systemic therapy. Your options may be slightly different, however. It is likely that you received oxaliplatin-based chemotherapy as part of initial treatment. CAPEOX and FOLFOX are oxaliplatin-based regimens. Oxaliplatin can cause serious nerve damage and should not be given too often. For this reason, if you've had recent treatment with FOLFOX or CAPEOX, you should not have more chemotherapy that includes oxaliplatin. The recommended options for systemic therapy are shown in Guide 6.

If you have not had recent treatment with FOLFOX or CAPEOX, your options for systemic therapy depend on prior chemotherapy received, whether the tumor has any biomarkers, and how well you are expected to tolerate certain systemic therapies. If one regimen stops working, there are other options that may work for you. These are called second- and third-line regimens.

Systemic therapy may shrink the tumors to a size small enough to be removed with surgery. If your doctors think that surgery might be possible, the size of the tumors will be checked

---

Guide 6
Systemic therapy for distant recurrence – recent treatment with FOLFOX or CAPEOX

Type of systemic therapy	Regimens
Chemotherapy	• FOLFIRI with or without a biologic • Irinotecan with or without a biologic Biologics include bevacizumab, ziv-aflibercept, ramucirumab, cetuximab,* and panitumumab* *For cancers without *RAS* or *BRAF* mutations
Immunotherapy (dMMR/MSI-H tumors only)	• Pembrolizumab (Keytruda) • Nivolumab (Opdivo) with or without ipilimumab (Yervoy)
Targeted therapy (*BRAF* V600E positive tumors)	• Encorafenib (Braftovi) + cetuximab (Erbitux) or panitumumab (Vectibix)

about every 2 months during systemic therapy. If the cancer does not become resectable, systemic therapy is typically continued. The goal is to slow the growth and spread of the cancer.

If the cancer becomes resectable, surgery is recommended. After surgery, most people will have more systemic therapy. Observation may be an option in some cases. If systemic therapy is planned, the regimen may be different from what you had before surgery. When there are no signs of cancer, you can resume surveillance.

Surgical treatment options

There are 2 options that include surgery for treating distant recurrences of colon cancer. Surgery is only an option if all of the tumors can be totally removed. The treatment pathways also include chemotherapy, either before or after surgery.

Surgery first

This option starts with surgery to remove the liver or lung tumors. Local therapies such as ablation or SBRT may be appropriate instead of surgery if there are a limited number of small metastases.

If you have not had any previous systemic therapy, the next step is chemotherapy with one of the following regimens:

> FOLFOX

> CAPEOX

> Capecitabine

> 5-FU/leucovorin

If you are being treated with bevacizumab (Avastin), it should be stopped 6 weeks before surgery. It increases the risk of stroke and bleeding, especially in adults over 65 years of age. Bevacizumab can be restarted 6 to 8 weeks after surgery. Otherwise, it can slow healing.

If you have received treatment with chemotherapy before, options include more chemotherapy and observation. If prior chemotherapy included oxaliplatin, observation is recommended. When there are no signs of cancer, you can resume follow-up care and surveillance.

Chemotherapy first

This option starts with chemotherapy to shrink the metastases. Regimens recommended at this time include FOLFOX, CAPEOX, capecitabine, and 5-FU/leucovorin. After 2 to 3 months of chemotherapy, the next step is surgery to remove the metastases. Local therapies such as ablation or SBRT may be appropriate instead of surgery if there are a limited number of small metastases.

More chemotherapy usually follows surgery. However, observation will be an option for some people. The chemotherapy regimens recommended for use before surgery are also recommended after surgery. When there are no signs of cancer, you can resume surveillance.

Key points

› Metastasis refers to the spread of cancer cells to distant areas.

› Colon cancer spreads most often to the liver, sometimes to the lungs, and less often to the abdomen or other areas.

› If metastases are present at the time of diagnosis, it is stage IV colon cancer.

› Most commonly, metastases develop after treatment for non-metastatic colon cancer. This is called distant recurrence.

› Surgery is preferred for removing liver or lung tumors, but is not often an option.

› Local therapies such as ablation and SBRT may be used in addition to or in place of surgery if all areas of cancer can be removed.

› Metastatic colon cancer that cannot be removed with surgery and/or local therapies is treated with systemic therapy.

› The presence of biomarkers helps guide treatment for metastatic colon cancer.

› Testing for *RAS* and *BRAF* mutations, HER2 amplification, and dMMR/MSI-H is recommended.

Supportive care is available for everyone with cancer. It isn't meant to treat the cancer, but rather to help with symptoms and make you more comfortable.

6
Survivorship

Survivorship focuses on the physical, emotional, and financial issues unique to cancer survivors. Managing the long-term side effects of cancer and its treatment, staying connected with your primary care doctor, and living a healthy lifestyle are important parts of survivorship.

Colon cancer survivors may experience both short- and long-term health effects of cancer and its treatment. The effects depend in part on the treatment(s) received. Surgery, systemic therapy (chemotherapy, targeted therapy, and immunotherapy), and radiation therapy all have unique potential side effects.

Staying connected with your primary care doctor and adopting healthy habits may help prevent or offset these effects. It can also help lower the risk of getting other types of cancer.

Cancer survivors face a unique financial burden. Paying for doctor visits, tests, and treatments can become unmanageable, especially for those with little or no health insurance. You may also have costs not directly related to treatment, such as travel expenses and the cost of childcare or missed work.

The term financial toxicity is used to describe the problems patients face related to the cost of medical care. Financial toxicity can affect your quality of life and access to needed health care. If you need help paying for your cancer care, financial assistance may be available. Talk with a patient navigator, your treatment team's social worker, and your hospital's financial services department. Several of the

resources listed on page 64 contain helpful information on paying for cancer care.

Your primary care doctor

After finishing cancer treatment, your primary care doctor will play an important role in your care. Your oncologist (cancer doctor) and primary care physician (PCP) should work together to make sure you get the follow-up care you need. Your oncologist will develop a written survivorship care plan that includes:

> A summary of your cancer treatment history

> A description of the late- and long-term side effects you could have

> Recommendations for monitoring for the return of cancer

> Information on when your care will be transferred to your PCP

> Clear roles and responsibilities for both your cancer doctor and your PCP

> Recommendations on your overall health and well-being

Help with side effects

Diarrhea or incontinence

Colon surgery can cause changes to your bowel habits. You may experience changes in the frequency or urgency of your bowel movements. Diarrhea refers to having frequent and watery bowel movements. Incontinence is the inability to control urination (urinary incontinence) or bowel movements (fecal incontinence). The following may help with these side effects:

> Anti-diarrhea medicines

> Changing your diet

> Strengthening your pelvic floor

> Wearing protective undergarments

Nerve damage

The chemotherapy drug oxaliplatin can cause nerve damage to your fingers and toes. Symptoms include numbness, cramping, tingling, or pain in these areas. Acupuncture and/or heat may help. If you have painful nerve damage, a drug called duloxetine (Cymbalta) may help.

Ostomy care

If you have an ostomy, you may want to join an ostomy support group. Another option is to see a health care provider that specializes in ostomy care, such as an ostomy nurse. People with ostomies can still live very active lifestyles. However, it's a good idea to talk to an ostomy professional before doing any intense physical activity.

Experts recommend eating a healthy diet, especially one that includes a lot of plant-based foods (vegetables, fruits, and whole grains).

Healthy habits

Monitoring for the return of cancer is important after finishing treatment. But, it is also important to keep up with other aspects of your health. Steps you can take to help prevent other health issues and to improve your quality of life are described next.

Cancer screening
Get screened for other types of cancer, such as breast, prostate, and skin cancer. Your primary care doctor can tell you what cancer screening tests you should have based on your age and risk level.

Other health care
Get other recommended health care for your age, such as blood pressure screening, hepatitis C screening, and immunizations (like the flu shot).

Diet and exercise
Leading a healthy lifestyle includes maintaining a healthy body weight. Try to exercise at a moderate intensity for at least 150 minutes per week. Talk to your doctor before starting a new exercise regimen.

Eat a healthy diet with lots of plant-based foods. A low glycemic load (GL) diet may help prevent the return of colon cancer. Low GL foods cause a slower and smaller rise in blood sugar levels compared to other carbohydrate-containing foods. Talk to your doctor about a low glycemic load diet.

Alcohol may increase the risk of certain cancers. Drink little to no alcohol.

Aspirin
Talk to your doctor about taking aspirin every day to help prevent the return of colorectal cancers.

Quit smoking
If you are a smoker, quit! Your doctor will be able to provide (or refer you for) counseling on how to stop smoking.

share with us.

Take our survey
And help make the
NCCN Guidelines for Patients
better for everyone!

NCCN.org/patients/comments

More information

For more information on cancer survivorship, the following are available at NCCN.org/patientguidelines:

> *Survivorship Care for Healthy Living*

> *Survivorship Care for Cancer-Related Late and Long-Term Effects*

These resources address many topics relevant to cancer survivors, including:

> Anxiety, depression, and distress

> Cognitive dysfunction

> Fatigue

> Pain

> Sexual problems

> Sleep disorders

> Healthy lifestyles

> Immunizations

> Employment, insurance, and disability concerns

Key points

> Survivorship focuses on the physical, emotional, and financial issues unique to cancer survivors.

> Your cancer doctor and primary care doctor should work together to make sure you get the follow-up care you need.

> A survivorship care plan is helpful in transitioning your care to your primary care doctor.

> Healthy habits, including exercising and eating right, play an important role in helping to prevent other diseases and second cancers.

7
Making treatment decisions

It's important to be comfortable with the cancer treatment you choose. This choice starts with having an open and honest conversation with your doctor.

It's your choice

In shared decision-making, you and your doctors share information, discuss the options, and agree on a treatment plan. It starts with an open and honest conversation between you and your doctor.

Treatment decisions are very personal. What is important to you may not be important to someone else.

Some things that may play a role in your decision-making:

> What you want and how that might differ from what others want

> Your religious and spiritual beliefs

> Your feelings about certain treatments like surgery or chemotherapy

> Your feelings about pain or side effects such as nausea and vomiting

> Cost of treatment, travel to treatment centers, and time away from work

> Quality of life and length of life

> How active you are and the activities that are important to you

Think about what you want from treatment. Discuss openly the risks and benefits of specific treatments and procedures. Weigh options and share concerns with your doctor. If you take the time to build a relationship with your doctor, it will help you feel supported when considering options and making treatment decisions.

Second opinion

It is normal to want to start treatment as soon as possible. While cancer can't be ignored, there is time to have another doctor review your test results and suggest a treatment plan. This is called getting a second opinion, and it's a normal part of cancer care. Even doctors get second opinions!

Things you can do to prepare:

> Check with your insurance company about its rules on second opinions. There may be out-of-pocket costs to see doctors who are not part of your insurance plan.

> Make plans to have copies of all your records sent to the doctor you will see for your second opinion.

Support groups

Many people diagnosed with cancer find support groups to be helpful. Support groups often include people at different stages of treatment. If your hospital or community doesn't have support groups for people with cancer, check out the websites listed in this book.

Questions to ask

Possible questions to ask your doctors are listed on the following pages. Feel free to use these or come up with your own. Be clear about your goals for treatment and find out what to expect from treatment. Use a notebook to record answers to your questions and keep track of all of your records.

Questions about treatment

1. Do you consult NCCN recommendations when considering options?

2. Are you suggesting options other than what NCCN recommends? If yes, why?

3. Do your suggested options include clinical trials? Please explain why.

4. How do my age, health, and other factors affect my options?

5. What if I am pregnant, or planning to become pregnant in the future?

6. What are the benefits and risks of each option? Does any option offer a cure or long-term cancer control?

7. How much will treatment cost? What does my insurance cover?

8. How long do I have to decide about treatment?

9. Who can I call on weekends or non-office hours if I have an urgent problem with my cancer or my cancer treatment?

10. Can you give me a copy of my pathology report and other test results?

Questions about non-metastatic colon cancer

1. Am I a candidate for surgery (colectomy)? Why or why not?

2. How much of my colon will be removed? How many lymph nodes will be removed?

3. Will I need a colostomy? If so, will it be temporary?

4. Which side effects of surgery are most likely?

5. Am I a candidate for minimally invasive surgery?

6. Will I need chemotherapy after surgery? For how long?

7. How do I prepare for surgery? Do I have to stop taking any of my medicines? Are there foods I will have to avoid?

8. When will I be able to return to my normal activities?

9. Is home care after treatment needed? If yes, what type?

10. How likely is the cancer to return after treatment with surgery?

Questions about stage IV colon cancer

1. Where has the cancer spread?

2. Am I a candidate for surgery? If not, is it possible that I'll become a candidate?

3. What treatment will I have before, during, or after surgery?

4. Am I a candidate for treatment with local therapies? Did an interventional oncologist/radiologist review my case?

5. Which systemic therapy regimen do you recommend for me? Why?

6. How will you know if systemic therapy is working? What if it stops working?

7. Does my cancer have any biomarkers? How does this affect my options?

8. What is my prognosis?

9. What can be done to prevent or relieve the side effects of treatment?

10. Am I a candidate for a clinical trial? Do you know of one I can join?

Questions to ask your care team about their experience

1. Do you only treat colon cancer? What else do you treat?

2. What is the experience of those on your team?

3. Will you be consulting with experts to discuss my care? Whom will you consult?

4. Are you board certified? If yes, in what area?

5. How many patients like me (of the same age, gender, race) have you treated?

6. How many procedures like the one you're suggesting have you done?

7. Is this treatment a major part of your practice?

8. How often is a complication expected? How many of your patients have had complications?

9. I would like to get a second opinion. Is there someone you recommend?

Resources

American Cancer Society
cancer.org/cancer/colon-rectal-cancer.html

Anal Cancer Foundation
analcancerfoundation.org

Bowel Cancer UK
bowelcanceruk.org.uk

Cancer.Net
cancer.net/cancer-types/colorectal-cancer

CancerCare
Cancercare.org

Cancer Hope Network
cancerhopenetwork.org

Cancer Support Community
cancersupportcommunity.org

Colon Cancer Coalition
coloncancercoalition.org

Colon Cancer Foundation
coloncancerfoundation.org

Colon Club
Colonclub.com

Colontown
colontown.org

Colorectal Cancer Alliance
ccalliance.org

Colorectal Cancer Canada
colorectalcancercanada.com

Fight Colorectal Cancer
FightColorectalCancer.org

Global Colon Cancer Association
globalcca.org

HPV Cancers Alliance
hpvalliance.org

Love Your Buns
Loveyourbuns.org

Meredith's Miracles
merediths-miracles.org

National Cancer Institute (NCI)
cancer.gov/types/colorectal

National Coalition for Cancer Survivorship
canceradvocacy.org/toolbox

PAN Foundation
panfoundation.org

U.S. National Library of Medicine Clinical Trials Database
clinicaltrials.gov

Words to know

abdomen
The belly area between the chest and pelvis.

ablation
A type of local therapy used to destroy tumors in the liver or lungs. Also called image-guided ablation.

adenocarcinoma
Cancer in cells that line organs and make fluids or hormones. The most common type of colon cancer.

adenoma
The most common type of polyp and is the most likely to form cancer cells. Also called adenomatous polyps.

anus
The opening at the end of the large bowel that allows stool to pass out of the body.

biomarkers
Specific features of cancer cells. Biomarkers can include proteins made in response to the cancer and changes (mutations) in the DNA of the cancer cells.

biopsy
Removal of small amounts of tissue or fluid to be tested for disease.

cancer grade
How closely the cancer cells look like normal cells when viewed under a microscope.

cancer stage
Rating of the growth and spread of tumors.

carcinoembryonic antigen (CEA)
A protein that gets released by some tumors and can be detected in blood as a tumor marker.

carcinoma in situ
Abnormal cells on the innermost layer of the colon wall. These cells may become cancer and spread into deeper layers of the colon wall.

catheter
A flexible tube inserted in the body to give treatment or drain fluid from the body.

clinical trial
Research on a test or treatment to assess its safety or how well it works.

colectomy
Surgery to remove a part of the colon.

colon
The first and longest section of the large bowel. Unused food is turned into stool in the colon.

colonoscope
A thin, long tube with a light and camera used to see the colon.

colonoscopy
Insertion of a thin tool into the colon to view or remove tissue.

colostomy
Surgery to connect a part of the colon to the outside of the abdomen and that allows stool to drain into a bag.

complete blood count (CBC)
A test of the number of blood cells.

computed tomography (CT)
A test that uses x-rays from many angles to make a picture of the inside of the body.

contrast
A substance put into your body to make clearer pictures during imaging tests.

embolization
Blockage of blood flow to a tumor with beads that emit either chemotherapy or radiation.

enema
Injection of liquid into the rectum to clear the bowel.

esophagus
The tube-shaped digestive organ between the mouth and stomach.

external beam radiation therapy (EBRT)
Treatment with high-energy rays received from a machine outside the body.

familial adenomatous polyposis (FAP)
An inherited medical condition that increases the risk of colon cancer.

infusion
A method of giving drugs slowly through a needle into a vein.

intensity-modulated radiation therapy (IMRT)
Radiation therapy that uses small beams of different strengths based on the thickness of the tissue.

interventional oncology/radiology
A medical specialty that uses imaging techniques to deliver minimally invasive cancer treatments.

intraoperative radiation therapy (IORT)
Radiation therapy that is given inside the body at the end of an operation.

invasive cancer
Cancer cells have grown into the second layer of the colon wall.

large intestine (bowel)
A long tube-shaped organ that forms the last part of the digestive system. Includes the colon, rectum, and anus.

laxative
Drugs used to clean out the intestines.

lymph
A clear fluid containing white blood cells.

lymph node
Small groups of special disease-fighting cells located throughout the body.

lymphadenectomy
Surgery to remove lymph nodes.

magnetic resonance imaging (MRI)
A test that uses a magnetic field and radio waves to make pictures of the insides of the body.

metastasectomy
Surgery to remove cancer that has spread far from the first tumor.

metastasis
The spread of cancer cells from the first (primary) tumor to a distant site.

microsatellite instability-high/mismatch repair deficient (MSI-H/dMMR)
A biomarker (feature) of some colon cancers that is used to guide treatment. Everyone with colon cancer should be tested for this biomarker.

mucosa
The innermost layer of the colon wall that comes into contact with food.

muscularis propria
The third layer of the colon wall made mostly of muscle.

mutation
An abnormal change in the instructions (DNA) within cells for making and controlling cells.

needle biopsy
Removal of tissue or fluid samples from the body with a needle.

observation
A period of testing for cancer growth.

pathologist
A doctor who specializes in testing cells and tissue to find disease.

pedunculated polyp
A polyp shaped like a mushroom with a stalk.

pelvis
The area between the hip bones.

polyp
An overgrowth of cells on the inner lining of the colon wall.

portal vein embolization
The blood vessel to the liver tumor is blocked causing the healthy part of the liver to grow larger.

positron emission tomography (PET)
Use of radioactive material to see the shape and function of body parts, and at times, highlight certain tumors within the body.

primary tumor
The first mass of cancer cells in the body.

progression
The growth or spread of cancer after being tested or treated.

radiologist
A doctor that specializes in interpreting imaging tests.

rectum
The last part of the large bowel. Stool is held here until it leaves the body.

recurrence
The return of cancer after a cancer-free period.

serosa
The outer layer of the colon wall.

sessile polyp
A polyp that is flat.

stereotactic body radiation therapy (SBRT)
A highly specialized type of radiation therapy. May be used to treat colon cancer that has spread to the liver, lungs, or bone.

stool
Unused food passed out of the body; also called feces.

submucosa
The second layer of the colon wall made mostly of connective tissue.

supportive care
Treatment for the symptoms or health conditions caused by cancer or cancer treatment.

surgical margin
The normal tissue around the edge of a tumor that is removed during surgery.

three-dimensional conformal radiation therapy (3D-CRT)
Radiation therapy that uses beams that match the shape of the tumor.

tumor biomarker testing
Testing tumor tissue to look for targetable features called biomarkers.

tumor deposit
The presence of tiny tumors where the lymph drains from the tumor.

NCCN Contributors

This patient guide is based on the NCCN Clinical Practice Guidelines in Oncology (NCCN Guidelines®) for Colon Cancer, Version 1.2022 – February 25, 2022. It was adapted, reviewed, and published with help from the following people:

Dorothy A. Shead, MS
Senior Director
Patient Information Operations

Erin Vidic, MA
Senior Medical Writer, Patient Information

Susan Kidney
Senior Graphic Design Specialist

The NCCN Clinical Practice Guidelines in Oncology (NCCN Guidelines®) for Colon Cancer, Version 1.2022 were developed by the following NCCN Panel Members:

Al B. Benson, III, MD/Chair
Robert H. Lurie Comprehensive Cancer Center of Northwestern University

Alan P. Venook, MD/Vice-Chair
UCSF Helen Diller Family Comprehensive Cancer Center

Mahmoud M. Al-Hawary, MD
University of Michigan Rogel Cancer Center

Nilofer Azad, MD
The Sidney Kimmel Comprehensive Cancer Center at Johns Hopkins

*Yi-Jen Chen, MD, PhD
City of Hope National Medical Center

Kristen K. Ciombor, MD
Vanderbilt-Ingram Cancer Center

Stacey Cohen, MD
Fred Hutchinson Cancer Research Center/ Seattle Cancer Care Alliance

Harry S. Cooper, MD
Fox Chase Cancer Center

Dustin Deming, MD
University of Wisconsin Carbone Cancer Center

Linda Farkas, MD
UT Southwestern Simmons Comprehensive Cancer Center

Ignacio Garrido-Laguna, MD, PhD
Huntsman Cancer Institute at the University of Utah

Jean L. Grem, MD
Fred & Pamela Buffett Cancer Center

Andrew Gunn, MD
O'Neal Comprehensive Cancer Center at UAB

J. Randolph Hecht, MD
UCLA Jonsson Comprehensive Cancer Center

Sarah Hoffe, MD
Moffitt Cancer Center

*Joleen Hubbard, MD
Mayo Clinic Cancer Center

Steven Hunt, MD
Siteman Cancer Center at Barnes-Jewish Hospital and Washington University School of Medicine

*William Jeck, MD
Duke Cancer Institute

Kimberly L. Johung, MD, PhD
Yale Cancer Center/Smilow Cancer Hospital

Natalie Kirilcuk, MD
Stanford Cancer Institute

Smitha Krishnamurthi, MD
Case Comprehensive Cancer Center/ University Hospitals Seidman Cancer Center and Cleveland Clinic Taussig Cancer Institute

Wells A. Messersmith, MD
University of Colorado Cancer Center

*Jeffrey Meyerhardt, MD, MPH
Dana-Farber Brigham and Women's Cancer Center

Eric D. Miller, MD, PhD
The Ohio State University Comprehensive Cancer Center - James Cancer Hospital and Solove Research Institute

Mary F. Mulcahy, MD
Robert H. Lurie Comprehensive Cancer Center of Northwestern University

Steven Nurkin, MD, MS
Roswell Park Comprehensive Cancer Center

Michael J. Overman, MD
The University of Texas MD Anderson Cancer Center

Aparna Parikh, MD
Massachusetts General Hospital Cancer Center

Hitendra Patel, MD
UC San Diego Moores Cancer Center

Katrina Pedersen, MD, MS
Siteman Cancer Center at Barnes-Jewish Hospital and Washington University School of Medicine

Elizabeth Raskin, MD
UC Davis Comprehensive Cancer Center

Leonard Saltz, MD
Memorial Sloan Kettering Cancer Center

Charles Schneider, MD
Abramson Cancer Center at the University of Pennsylvania

David Shibata, MD
The University of Tennessee Health Science Center

John M. Skibber, MD
The University of Texas MD Anderson Cancer Center

*Constantinos T. Sofocleous, MD, PhD
Memorial Sloan Kettering Cancer Center

Elena M. Stoffel, MD, MPH
University of Michigan Rogel Cancer Center

Eden Stotsky-Himelfarb, BSN, RN
The Sidney Kimmel Comprehensive Cancer Center at Johns Hopkins

Christopher G. Willett, MD
Duke Cancer Institute

NCCN Staff

Kristina Gregory, RN, MSN, OCN
Vice President, Clinical Information Programs

Lisa Gurski, PhD
Manager, Licensed Clinical Content

* Reviewed this patient guide. For disclosures, visit NCCN.org/disclosures.

NCCN Cancer Centers

Abramson Cancer Center
at the University of Pennsylvania
Philadelphia, Pennsylvania
800.789.7366 • pennmedicine.org/cancer

Case Comprehensive Cancer Center/
University Hospitals Seidman Cancer
Center and Cleveland Clinic Taussig
Cancer Institute
Cleveland, Ohio
800.641.2422 • UH Seidman Cancer Center
uhhospitals.org/services/cancer-services
866.223.8100 • CC Taussig Cancer Institute
my.clevelandclinic.org/departments/cancer
216.844.8797 • Case CCC
case.edu/cancer

City of Hope National Medical Center
Los Angeles, California
800.826.4673 • cityofhope.org

Dana-Farber/Brigham and Women's
Cancer Center | Massachusetts General
Hospital Cancer Center
Boston, Massachusetts
617.732.5500 • youhaveus.org
617.726.5130
massgeneral.org/cancer-center

Duke Cancer Institute
Durham, North Carolina
888.275.3853 • dukecancerinstitute.org

Fox Chase Cancer Center
Philadelphia, Pennsylvania
888.369.2427 • foxchase.org

Fred & Pamela Buffett Cancer Center
Omaha, Nebraska
402.559.5600 • unmc.edu/cancercenter

Fred Hutchinson Cancer Center
Seattle, Washington
206.667.5000 • fredhutch.org

Huntsman Cancer Institute
at the University of Utah
Salt Lake City, Utah
800.824.2073 • huntsmancancer.org

Indiana University
Melvin and Bren Simon
Comprehensive Cancer Center
Indianapolis, Indiana
888.600.4822 • www.cancer.iu.edu

Mayo Clinic Cancer Center
Phoenix/Scottsdale, Arizona
Jacksonville, Florida
Rochester, Minnesota
480.301.8000 • Arizona
904.953.0853 • Florida
507.538.3270 • Minnesota
mayoclinic.org/cancercenter

Memorial Sloan Kettering
Cancer Center
New York, New York
800.525.2225 • mskcc.org

Moffitt Cancer Center
Tampa, Florida
888.663.3488 • moffitt.org

O'Neal Comprehensive
Cancer Center at UAB
Birmingham, Alabama
800.822.0933 • uab.edu/onealcancercenter

Robert H. Lurie Comprehensive Cancer
Center of Northwestern University
Chicago, Illinois
866.587.4322 • cancer.northwestern.edu

Roswell Park Comprehensive
Cancer Center
Buffalo, New York
877.275.7724 • roswellpark.org

Siteman Cancer Center at Barnes-
Jewish Hospital and Washington
University School of Medicine
St. Louis, Missouri
800.600.3606 • siteman.wustl.edu

St. Jude Children's
Research Hospital/
The University of Tennessee
Health Science Center
Memphis, Tennessee
866.278.5833 • stjude.org
901.448.5500 • uthsc.edu

Stanford Cancer Institute
Stanford, California
877.668.7535 • cancer.stanford.edu

The Ohio State University
Comprehensive Cancer Center -
James Cancer Hospital and
Solove Research Institute
Columbus, Ohio
800.293.5066 • cancer.osu.edu

The Sidney Kimmel Comprehensive
Cancer Center at Johns Hopkins
Baltimore, Maryland
410.955.8964
www.hopkinskimmelcancercenter.org

The University of Texas
MD Anderson Cancer Center
Houston, Texas
844.269.5922 • mdanderson.org

UC Davis
Comprehensive Cancer Center
Sacramento, California
916.734.5959 • 800.770.9261
health.ucdavis.edu/cancer

UC San Diego Moores Cancer Center
La Jolla, California
858.822.6100 • cancer.ucsd.edu

UCLA Jonsson
Comprehensive Cancer Center
Los Angeles, California
310.825.5268 • cancer.ucla.edu

UCSF Helen Diller Family
Comprehensive Cancer Center
San Francisco, California
800.689.8273 • cancer.ucsf.edu

University of Colorado Cancer Center
Aurora, Colorado
720.848.0300 • coloradocancercenter.org

University of Michigan
Rogel Cancer Center
Ann Arbor, Michigan
800.865.1125 • rogelcancercenter.org

University of Wisconsin
Carbone Cancer Center
Madison, Wisconsin
608.265.1700 • uwhealth.org/cancer

UT Southwestern Simmons
Comprehensive Cancer Center
Dallas, Texas
214.648.3111 • utsouthwestern.edu/simmons

Vanderbilt-Ingram Cancer Center
Nashville, Tennessee
877.936.8422 • vicc.org

Yale Cancer Center/
Smilow Cancer Hospital
New Haven, Connecticut
855.4.SMILOW • yalecancercenter.org

Notes

Contents

Introduction

Like you, we love fabric! And the more fabrics, the merrier.

When we were just starting our business, we bought small cuts of fabric to build our stash, because that's all we could afford. As we designed more quilts, we needed more and more fabric. Finally, we gave in and opened a retail store in the chicken coop where we had based our pattern headquarters on the Country Threads farm. We knew nothing about running or buying for a retail store, but we had shopped in many so we knew what we wanted.

At the time, dark and primitive was the popular look and we loved it! Slowly but surely, fabric trends shifted to lighter and brighter, until today dark and primitive can be hard to find. And we're embracing this look too!

But that doesn't mean we aren't still true to the Country Threads scrappy look. As a shop that was known for selling kits and running fabric clubs, we couldn't rely on using just two or three fabrics in a quilt. We'd run out of the featured fabrics after making just a couple of kits if we needed two or three yards per quilt. That's why we began cutting eighth-yards and fat quarters so we could include a little bit of many fabrics in each quilt kit. If a quilt required two yards of red fabric, substituting eight quarter-yard cuts of assorted reds was more exciting to us! The kits were so beautiful that they were hard to resist and many of our past customers still tell us today that they have kits waiting to be sewn.

Thus, the Country Threads look was born out of necessity and creativity. So, when we decided to update some of our tried-and-true patterns with today's lighter and brighter color palette, you can rest assured, the quilts are still scrappy!

If you're new to Country Threads—welcome! And if you're a longtime friend, we're happy you're still a fan after 40 years! Our hope is that you will have just as much fun making these quilts as we did.

~Mary and Connie

Feathered to a T

FINISHED QUILT: 46¼" × 46¼"   FINISHED BLOCK: 11¼" × 11¼"

Capital T blocks came into vogue during the temperance movement (an attempt to prevent the consumption of alcohol, which led to Prohibition in the United States). But take a look at this thoroughly modern feathered version.

Materials

Yardage is based on 42"-wide fabric.

- 1⅝ yards *total* of assorted cream prints for blocks and outer border
- 1⅛ yards *total* of assorted blue prints for blocks
- ½ yard of light print A for sashing
- ⅛ yard of light print B for cornerstones
- ⅝ yard of blue dot for inner border and binding
- 3 yards of fabric for backing
- 53" × 53" piece of batting

Cutting

All measurements include ¼" seam allowances. As you cut, keep like pieces together.

From the assorted cream prints, cut:

9 *sets of 2* matching squares, 4⅝" × 4⅝"; cut each set of squares in half diagonally to yield 4 large triangles (36 total)

108 squares, 2⅛" × 2⅛"; cut each square in half diagonally to yield 216 small triangles

9 *sets of 4* matching pieces, 1¾" × 4¼" (36 total)

Various lengths of 2½"-wide pieces to total 195"

From the assorted blue prints, cut:

9 *sets of 2* matching squares, 4⅝" × 4⅝"; cut each set of squares in half diagonally to yield 4 large triangles (36 total)

108 squares, 2⅛" × 2⅛"; cut each square in half diagonally to yield 216 small triangles

9 squares, 4¼" × 4¼"

From light print A, cut:

8 strips, 2" × 42"; crosscut into 24 strips, 2" × 11¾"

From light print B, cut:

1 strip, 2" × 42"; crosscut into 16 squares, 2" × 2"

From the blue dot, cut:

5 strips, 2¼" × 42"

5 strips, 1½" × 42"

Pieced and quilted by Mary Etherington

Making the Blocks

Press seam allowances in the directions indicated by the arrows.

1 Sew the cream and blue large triangles together in pairs to make half-square-triangle units that are 4¼" square, including seam allowances. Make nine sets of four matching units (36 total).

Make 9 sets of
4 matching units,
4¼" × 4¼".

2 Sew the cream and blue small triangles together in pairs to make half-square-triangle units that are 1¾" square, including seam allowances. Make 216 units.

Make 216 units,
1¾" × 1¾".

3 Lay out six small triangle units from step 2 and one cream 1¾" × 4¼" piece as shown. Join the triangle units to make two rows. Sew the rows to opposite sides of the cream piece to make a side unit measuring 4¼" square, including seam allowances. Make 36 side units.

Make 36 units,
4¼" × 4¼".

4 Lay out four matching large triangle units from step 1, four side units from step 3, and one blue 4¼" square in three rows. Sew all the pieces into rows and then join the rows. Make nine blocks measuring 11¾" square, including seam allowances.

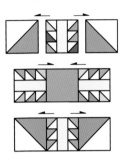 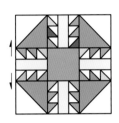

Make 9 blocks,
11¾" × 11¾".

Assembling the Quilt Top

1 Join three light A strips and four light B squares to make a sashing row. Make four rows that measure 2" × 40¼", including seam allowances.

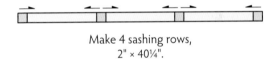

Make 4 sashing rows,
2" × 40¼".

2 Join four light A strips and three blocks to make a block row. Make three rows measuring 11¾" × 40¼", including seam allowances.

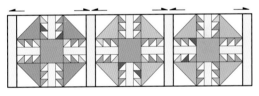

Make 3 block rows,
11¾" × 40¼".

3 Join the sashing and block rows, alternating them as shown in the quilt assembly diagram on page 10. The quilt-top center should measure 40¼" square, including seam allowances.

4 Join the blue dot 1½"-wide strips end to end. From the pieced strip, cut two 42¼"-long and two 40¼"-long strips. Sew the shorter strips to the left and right sides of the quilt center. Sew the longer strips to the top and bottom edges. The quilt top should measure 42¼" square, including seam allowances.

5 Join the light 2½"-wide pieces end to end to make two 46¼"-long strips and two 42¼"-long strips. Press the seam allowances in one direction. Sew the shorter strips to the left and right sides of the quilt center. Sew the longer strips to the top and bottom edges. The quilt top should measure 46¼" square.

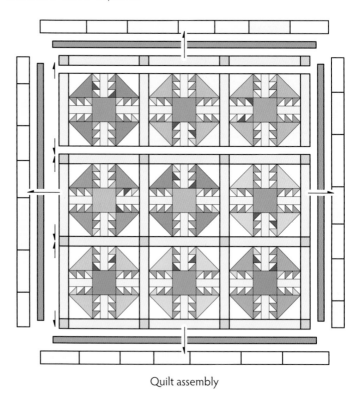

Quilt assembly

Finishing the Quilt

Visit ShopMartingale.com/HowtoQuilt for free downloadable information on any finishing steps.

1 Layer the quilt top with the batting and backing. Baste the layers together.

2 Quilt by hand or machine. The quilt shown is machine quilted with parallel horizontal lines stitched from edge to edge and spaced roughly ½" apart.

3 Use the blue dot 2¼"-wide strips to make double-fold binding. Attach the binding to the quilt.

Iowa Roads

FINISHED QUILT: 52½" × 52½"   **FINISHED BLOCK:** 12" × 12"

The back roads in our state will take you to small towns with lots of personality, each unique in its own way. Using a scrappy assortment of fall-color prints adds a one-of-a-kind look to the blocks of this cozy throw that's perfect to bring along on a visit to the pumpkin patch.

Materials

Yardage is based on 42"-wide fabric. Fat eighths measure 9" × 21". Fat quarters measure 18" × 21".

- 11 fat eighths of assorted light prints for blocks and star units
- 6 fat quarters of assorted light prints for sashing and star units
- 17 fat eighths of assorted orange prints for blocks and sashing
- 11 fat quarters of assorted gray prints for blocks, sashing units, and binding
- 4 fat eighths of assorted gray prints for blocks
- 16 fat eighths of assorted black prints for star units
- 3⅜ yards of fabric for backing
- 59" × 59" piece of batting

Cutting

All measurements include ¼" seam allowances. As you cut, keep like pieces together. Cutting for the small triangles is for traditional piecing. If you prefer to use paper foundations, you'll need papers that yield 2" finished half-square-triangle units. Follow the instructions with the papers rather than cutting the fat eighths into triangles as directed below.

Cutting for Blocks

From *each of 9* assorted light fat eighths, cut:
8 squares, 2⅞" × 2⅞"; cut in half diagonally to yield 16 triangles (144 total)

From *each of 5* assorted orange fat eighths, cut:
8 squares, 2⅞" × 2⅞"; cut in half diagonally to yield 16 triangles (80 total)

From *each of 5* assorted orange fat eighths, cut:
4 pieces, 2½" × 8½" (20 total)

From 1 orange print fat eighth, cut:
16 squares, 2½" × 2½"

From *each of 4* assorted gray fat quarters, cut:
8 squares, 2⅞" × 2⅞"; cut in half diagonally to yield 16 triangles (64 total)

From *each of 4* assorted gray fat eighths, cut:
4 pieces, 2½" × 8½" (16 total)

From 1 gray print fat quarter, cut:
20 squares, 2½" × 2½"

Cutting for Sashing Units, Star Units, and Binding

From *each of 6* assorted light fat quarters, cut:
24 pieces, 2½" × 4½" (144 total)

From the remainder of the assorted light fat eighths, cut *matching sets*:
16 sets of 4 pieces, 1½" × 2½" (64 total)
16 sets of 4 squares, 1½" × 1½" (64 total)

From *each of 6* assorted orange fat eighths, cut:
24 squares, 2½" × 2½" (144 total)

From *each of 6* assorted gray fat quarters, cut:
24 squares, 2½" × 2½" (144 total)

From the remainder of the assorted gray fat quarters, cut:
11 strips, 2¼" × 21"

From *each* of the black fat eighths, cut:
1 square, 2½" × 2½" (16 total)
8 squares, 1½" × 1½" (128 total)

Making the Blocks

Press seam allowances in the directions indicated by the arrows.

1 Sew a light triangle to an orange triangle to make a half-square-triangle unit measuring 2½" square, including seam allowances. Make five sets of 16 matching units (80 total).

Make 5 sets of
16 matching units,
2½" × 2½".

2 Sew a light triangle to a gray triangle to make a half-square-triangle unit measuring 2½" square, including seam allowances. Make four sets of 16 matching units (64 total).

Make 4 sets of
16 matching units,
2½" × 2½".

3 Lay out 16 matching orange triangle units from step 1 in four rows. Sew the units into rows and then join the rows. Make five orange block centers measuring 8½" square, including seam allowances.

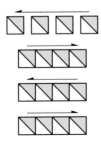

Make 5 block centers,
8½" × 8½".

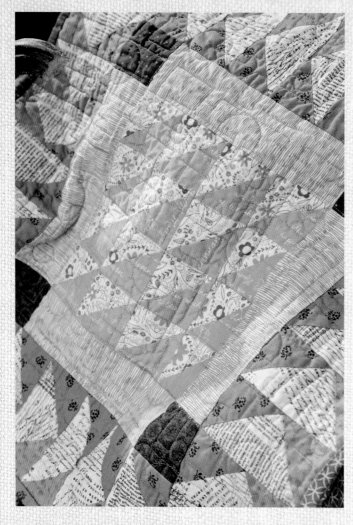

4 Lay out four gray 2½" squares, four matching orange 2½" × 8½" pieces, and one orange block center from step 3 in three rows. Sew all the pieces into rows and then join the rows. Make five orange blocks measuring 12½" square, including seam allowances.

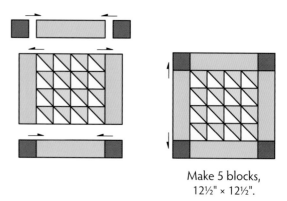

Make 5 blocks,
12½" × 12½".

5 Lay out 16 matching gray triangle units from step 2 in four rows. Sew the units into rows and then join the rows. Make four gray block centers measuring 8½" square, including seam allowances.

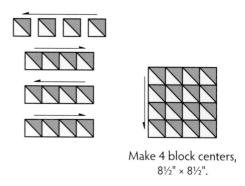

Make 4 block centers,
8½" × 8½".

6 Lay out four orange 2½" squares, four matching gray 2½" × 8½" pieces, and one gray block center from step 5 in three rows. Sew all the pieces into rows and then join the rows. Make four gray blocks measuring 12½" square, including seam allowances.

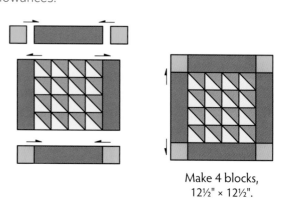

Make 4 blocks,
12½" × 12½".

Making the Sashing Units

1 Draw a diagonal line from corner to corner on the wrong side of the orange and gray 2½" squares. Place a marked orange square on the left end of a light 2½" × 4½" piece, right sides together. Sew on the marked line. Trim the outside corner of the square ¼" from the stitched line. Place a marked gray square on the right end of the light piece. Sew and trim as before to make a flying-geese unit measuring 2½" × 4½", including seam allowances. Make five sets of 24 matching units.

Make 5 sets of
24 matching units,
2½" × 4½".

2 Join six matching units from step 1 as shown to make sashing unit A measuring 4½" × 12½", including seam allowances. Make five sets of four matching A units.

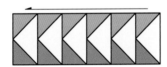

Make 5 sets of 4 matching A units,
4½" × 12½".

3 Using the remaining marked orange and gray squares from step 1, place a marked gray square on the left end of a light 2½" × 4½" piece, right sides together. Repeat step 1 to sew and trim. Place a marked orange square on the right end of the light piece. Sew and trim to make a flying-geese unit measuring 2½" × 4½", including seam allowances. Make 24 matching units.

Make 24 units,
2½" × 4½".

4 Join six units from step 3, noting the orientation of the units, to make sashing unit B. Make four matching B units measuring 4½" × 12½", including seam allowances.

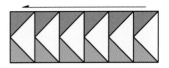

Make 4 matching B units,
4½" × 12½".

Making the Star Units

1 Draw a diagonal line from corner to corner on the wrong side of eight matching black 1½" squares. Place a marked square on one end of a light 1½" × 2½" piece, right sides together. Sew on the marked line. Trim the outside corner of the square ¼" from the stitched line. Place a marked square on the opposite end of the light piece. Sew and trim as before to make a flying-geese unit measuring 1½" × 2½", including seam allowances. Repeat to make 16 sets of four matching units.

Make 16 sets of
4 matching units,
1½" × 2½".

2 Lay out four light 1½" squares, four matching flying-geese units from step 1, and one black 2½" square in three rows. The light and black prints should be the same throughout. Sew all the pieces into rows and then join the rows. Make 16 star units measuring 4½" square, including seam allowances.

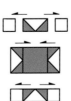

Make 16 units,
4½" × 4½".

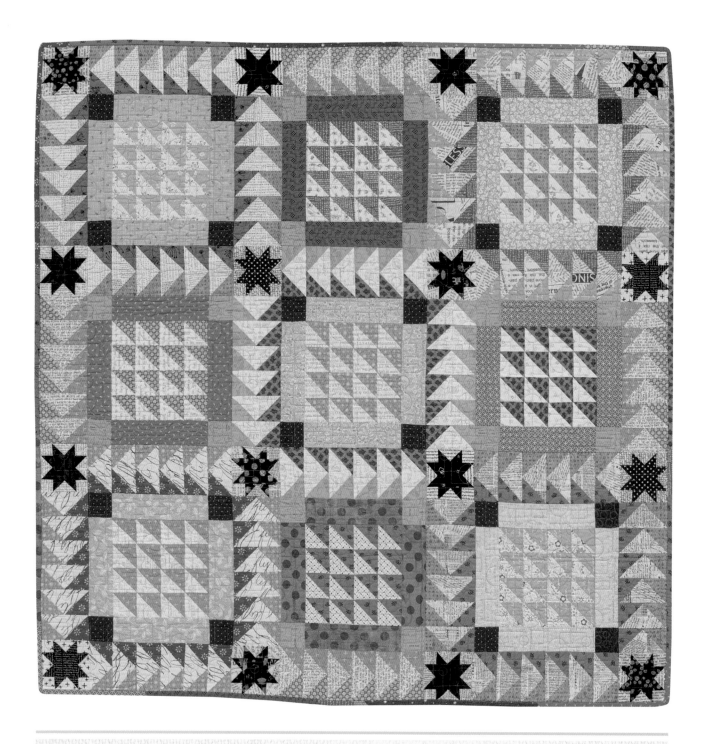

Pieced by Connie Tesene; quilted by Mary Etherington

Assembling the Quilt Top

Refer to the photo on page 16 and the quilt assembly diagram below as needed throughout.

1 On a design wall, lay out the orange and gray blocks in three rows, alternating them so that the top and bottom rows start with an orange block and the center rows start with a gray block. Position four matching sashing A units around each of the orange blocks with the gray triangles next to the block.

2 Place sashing B units along the top and bottom edges and along the left and right sides of the center row. The orange triangles should be next to the gray blocks. Place a star unit between each of the sashing units.

3 For the sashing rows, join four star units and three sashing units to make a row. Make four rows measuring 4½" × 52½", including seam allowances.

4 For the block rows, join four sashing units and three blocks to make a row. Make three rows measuring 12½" × 52½", including seam allowances.

5 Join the sashing and block rows, alternating them as shown in the quilt assembly diagram. The quilt top should measure 52½" square.

Finishing the Quilt

Visit ShopMartingale.com/HowtoQuilt for free downloadable information on any finishing steps.

1 Layer the quilt top with the batting and backing. Baste the layers together.

2 Quilt by hand or machine. The quilt shown is machine quilted with an allover boxes and circles design.

3 Sew the gray 2¼" × 21" strips together end to end to make a scrappy double-fold binding. Attach the binding to the quilt.

Quilt assembly

Spring Days

FINISHED QUILT: 84½" × 96½"   **FINISHED BLOCK: 12" × 12"**

Hints of greens emerging from the ground and on tree branches are a sign that spring can't be far away. That fires us up to refresh our interior spaces with lighter, brighter colors. If you've been saving a favorite large-scale print, here's a pattern to showcase that beloved print at its best!

Materials

Yardage is based on 42"-wide fabric.

- 3½ yards *total* of assorted medium and dark prints (referred to collectively as "dark") for blocks
- 3½ yards *total* of assorted light prints for blocks
- 3⅜ yards of green floral for setting squares and binding
- 7¾ yards of fabric for backing
- 93" × 105" piece of batting

Cutting

All measurements include ¼" seam allowances.

From the assorted dark prints, cut a *total* of:

74 squares, 6⅞" × 6⅞"; cut in half diagonally to yield 148 triangles

From the assorted light prints, cut a *total* of:

74 squares, 6⅞" × 6⅞"; cut in half diagonally to yield 148 triangles

From the green floral, cut:

7 strips, 12½" × 42"; crosscut into 19 squares, 12½" × 12½"

10 strips, 2¼" × 42"

Making the Blocks

Press seam allowances in the directions indicated by the arrows.

1 Sew a light triangle to a dark triangle to make a half-square-triangle unit. Make 148 units measuring 6½" square, including seam allowances.

Make 148 units, 6½" × 6½".

2 Lay out four half-square-triangle units in two rows, with the dark triangles all pointing in the same direction. Sew the units into rows and then join the rows. Make 37 blocks measuring 12½" square, including seam allowances.

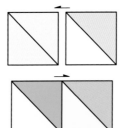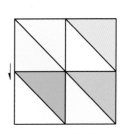

Make 37 blocks, 12½" × 12½".

Assembling the Quilt Top

Referring to the quilt assembly diagram, lay out the blocks and green squares in eight rows. Sew the blocks and squares into rows and then join the rows. The quilt top should measure 84½" × 96½".

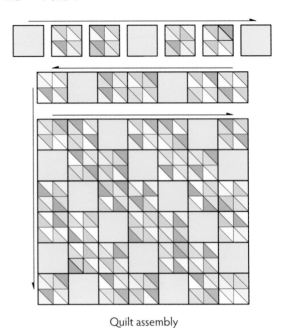

Quilt assembly

Finishing the Quilt

Visit ShopMartingale.com/HowtoQuilt for free downloadable information on any finishing steps.

1 Layer the quilt top with the batting and backing. Baste the layers together.

2 Hand or machine quilt. The quilt shown is machine quilted with an allover design of intersecting circles.

3 Use the green 2¼"-wide strips to make double-fold binding. Attach the binding to the quilt.

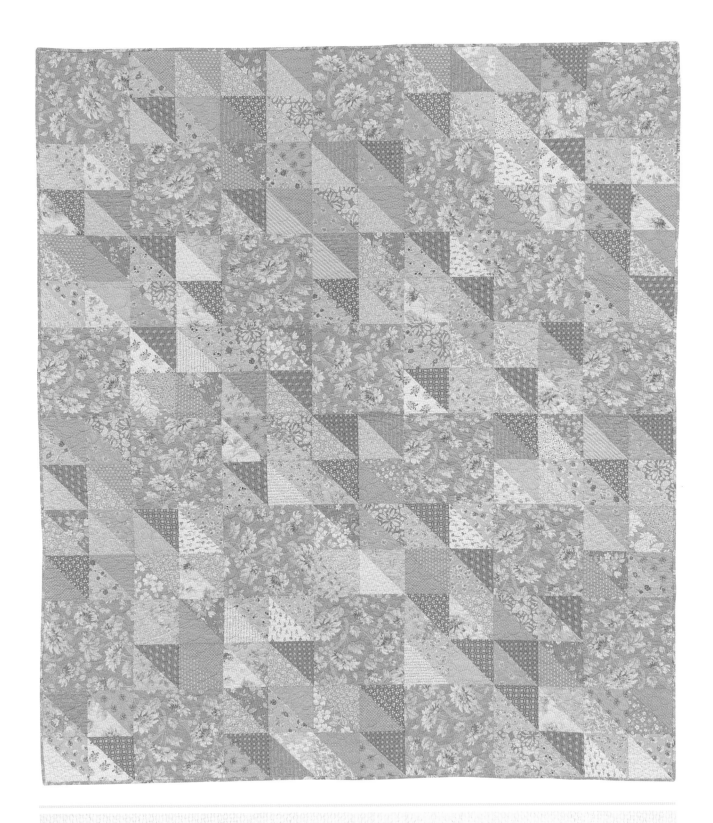

Pieced by Connie Tesene; quilted by Calico Hutch

Song of Spring

FINISHED QUILT: 21½" × 21½"   FINISHED BLOCK: 3" × 3"

Flowers are blooming and birds are chirping, singing the song of spring. And here's a secret a little birdie told us about this cutie. It's a small-scale variation of Spring Days (page 19). If you have a stash of small scraps you couldn't part with, here's your chance to stitch them into a tiny treasure.

Materials

Yardage is based on 42"-wide fabric.

- ⅓ yard *total* of assorted medium and dark prints (referred to collectively as "dark") for blocks
- ⅓ yard *total* of assorted light prints for blocks
- ⅓ yard of blue floral for setting squares
- ¼ yard of red tone on tone for binding
- ¾ yards of fabric for backing
- 26" × 26" piece of batting

Cutting

All measurements include ¼" seam allowances.

From the assorted dark prints, cut a *total* of:
64 squares, 2⅜" × 2⅜"; cut in half diagonally to yield 128 triangles

From the assorted light prints, cut a *total* of:
64 squares, 2⅜" × 2⅜"; cut in half diagonally to yield 128 triangles

From the blue floral, cut:
2 strips, 3½" × 42"; crosscut into 17 squares, 3½" × 3½"

From the red tone on tone, cut:
3 strips, 1½" × 42"

Making the Blocks

Press seam allowances in the directions indicated by the arrows.

1 Join light and dark triangles to make 128 half-square-triangle units measuring 2" square, including seam allowances.

Make 128 units,
2" × 2".

2 Lay out four triangle units in two rows, with the dark triangles all pointing in the same direction. Sew the units into rows and then join the rows. Make 32 blocks measuring 3½" square, including seam allowances.

Make 32 blocks,
3½" × 3½".

Pieced and quilted by Connie Tesene

Assembling and Finishing the Quilt

Visit ShopMartingale.com/HowtoQuilt for free downloadable information on any finishing steps.

1 Referring to the quilt assembly diagram below, lay out the blocks and blue squares in seven rows. Sew the blocks and squares into rows and then join the rows. The quilt top should measure 21½" square.

2 Layer the quilt top with the batting and backing. Baste the layers together. Hand or machine quilt. The quilt shown is machine quilted with horizontal parallel lines stitched from edge to edge.

3 Use the red 1½"-wide strips to make single-fold binding. Attach the binding to the quilt.

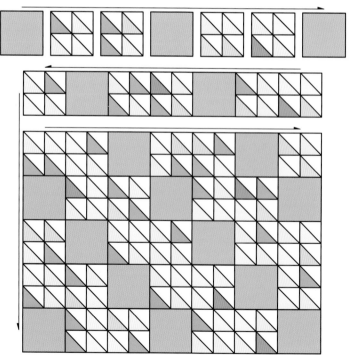

Quilt assembly

Cherry Baskets

FINISHED QUILT: 44½" × 44½"   FINISHED BLOCK: 12" × 12"

A tisket, a tasket, we've sewn pink cherry baskets! Soft florals reminiscent of the 1930s and 1940s set the tone for a sweet-as-can-be wall hanging that's easy to appliqué using your favorite method. We searched our button boxes to top each basket with a trio of hand-picked favorites for an added touch.

Materials

Yardage is based on 42"-wide fabric. Fat quarters measure 18" × 21".

- 2½ yards *total* of assorted light prints for blocks, border, and binding
- 9 fat quarters of assorted pink prints for basket appliqués
- 2⅞ yards of fabric for backing
- 51" × 51" piece of batting
- 27 assorted red buttons for cherries

Cutting

All measurements include ¼" seam allowances.

From the assorted light prints, cut a *total* of:

9 squares, 13¼" × 13¼"

19 strips, 2¼" × 10"

80 pieces, 2½" × 4½"

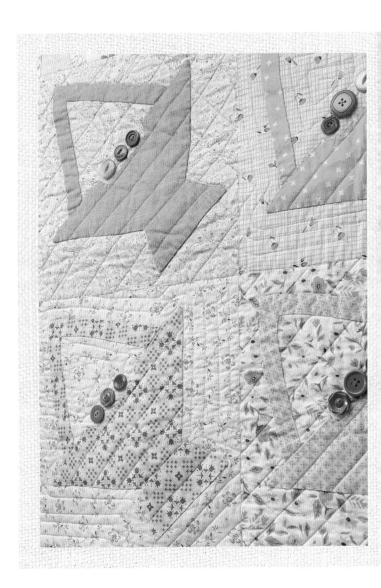

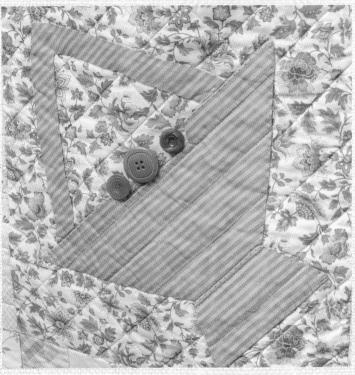

Making the Blocks

1 Using your favorite appliqué method and referring to the patterns on pages 30 and 31, prepare the basket, handle, and base for appliqué. Mary used turned-edge appliqué and stitched the baskets to the blocks with a machine blind hem stitch to mimic the look of hand appliqué.

2 Fold a light square in half diagonally and lightly finger-press to establish a center crease. Using matching pink shapes, appliqué a basket, handle, and base on each light square, starting with the handle. Make nine blocks and trim them to 12½" square, including seam allowances.

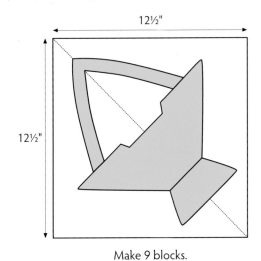

Make 9 blocks.

Assembling the Quilt Top

Press seam allowances in the directions indicated by the arrows.

1 Referring to the quilt assembly diagram on page 29, lay out the blocks in three rows of three blocks each. Sew the blocks into rows and then join the rows. The quilt top should measure 36½" square, including seam allowances.

2 Join 18 light 2½" × 4½" pieces to make a side border measuring 4½" × 36½", including seam allowances. Make two. Join 22 light pieces to make a top border measuring 4½" × 44½", including seam allowances. Repeat to make a bottom border.

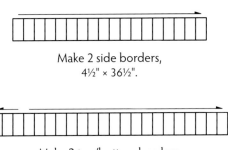

Make 2 side borders,
4½" × 36½".

Make 2 top/bottom borders,
4½" × 44½".

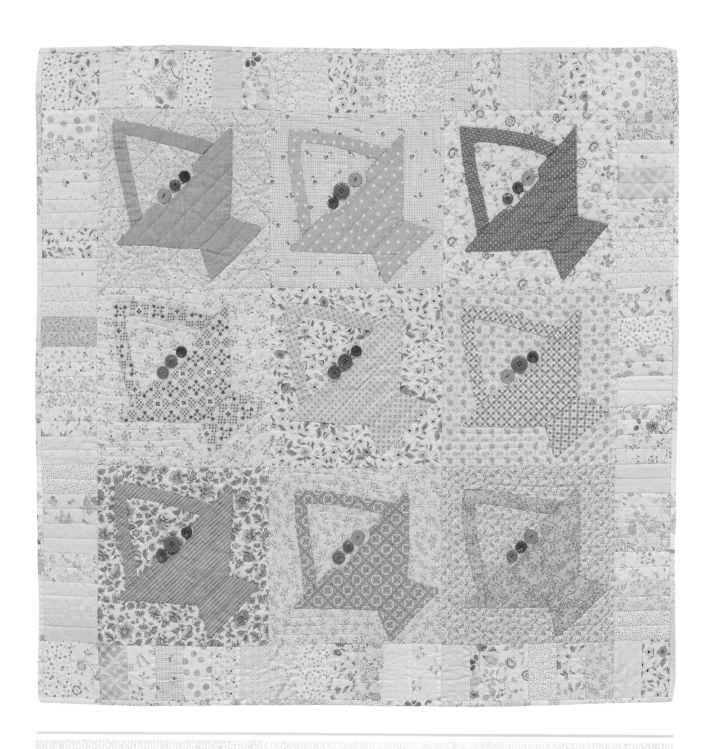

Pieced by Mary Etherington; quilted by Sue Urich

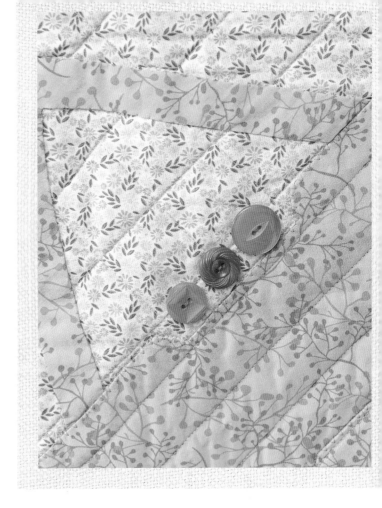

3 Sew the shorter borders to the left and right sides of the quilt top. Sew the longer borders to the top and bottom edges. The quilt top should measure 44½" square.

Finishing the Quilt

Visit ShopMartingale.com/HowtoQuilt for free downloadable information on any finishing steps.

1 Layer the quilt top with the batting and backing. Baste the layers together.

2 Quilt by hand or machine. The quilt shown is machine quilted with parallel diagonal lines in the baskets. The block backgrounds are quilted in various ways including echo quilting around some of the baskets. The borders are quilted with a straight line through each patchwork strip.

3 Sew three red buttons to each basket block, placing them along the indent at the top of the basket.

4 Use the light 2¼" × 10" strips to make scrappy double-fold binding. Attach the binding to the quilt.

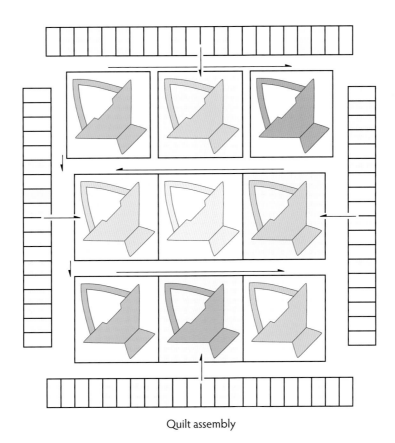

Quilt assembly

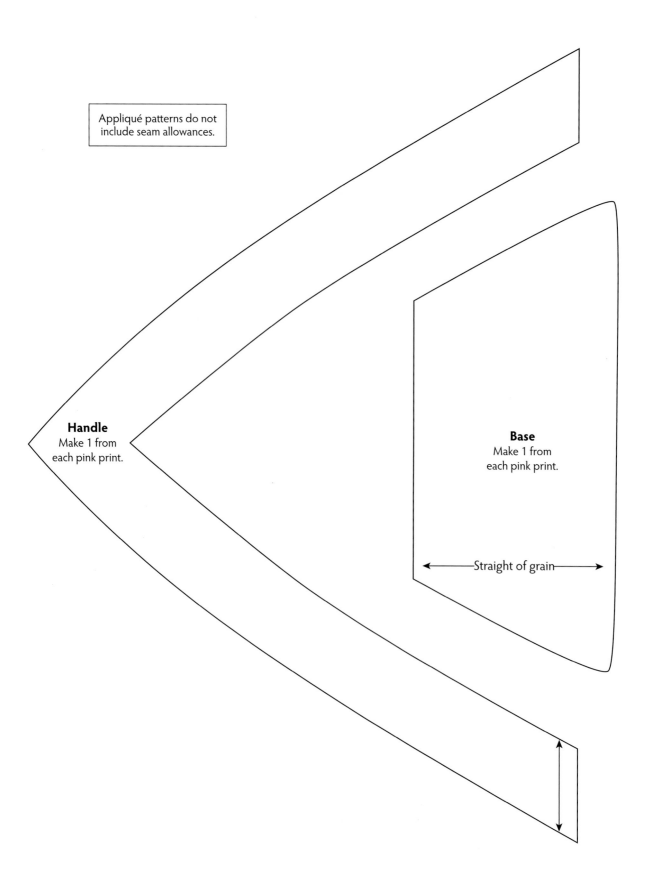

Appliqué patterns do not include seam allowances.

Handle
Make 1 from each pink print.

Base
Make 1 from each pink print.

Straight of grain

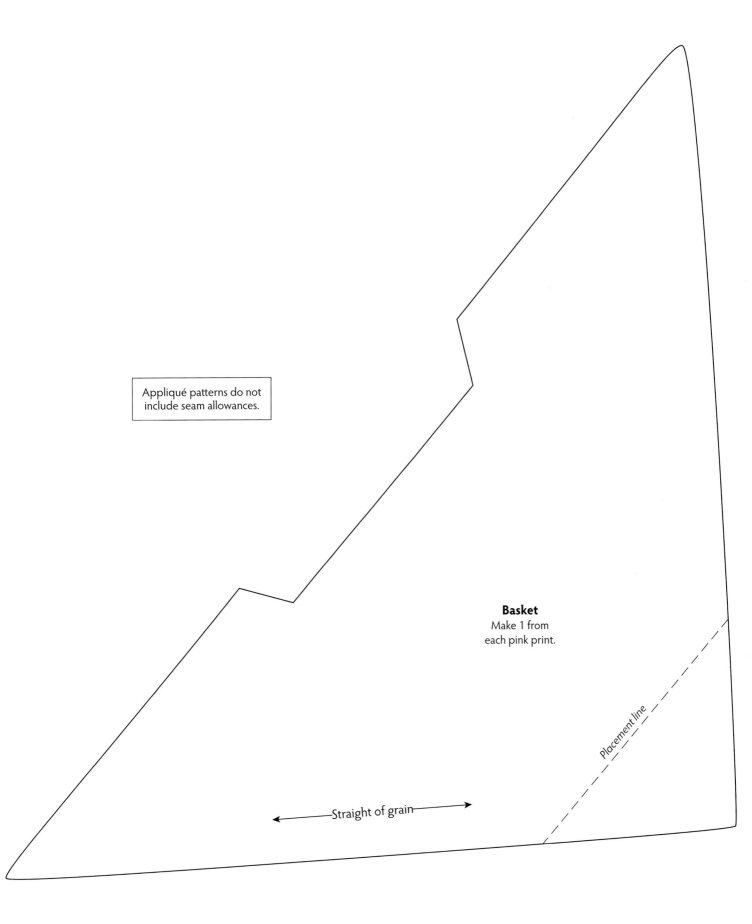

Appliqué patterns do not
include seam allowances.

Basket
Make 1 from
each pink print.

Placement line

←————— Straight of grain —————→

Wind Farm

FINISHED QUILT: 66½" × 85½"   FINISHED BLOCK: 16" × 16"

Corn may be Iowa's number one crop, but the state is also the leader in wind energy! These days, it's a common sight to see giant wind turbines harvesting all that wind and converting it into more than half of the state's electricity. Why not convert your favorite scraps into this fun pinwheel quilt?

Materials

Yardage is based on 42"-wide fabric. Fat quarters are 18" × 21".

- 12 fat quarters of assorted light prints for blocks
- 12 fat quarters of assorted medium and dark prints (referred to collectively as "dark") for blocks and sashing
- ⅞ yard of gray print for blocks
- 3½ yards of blue solid for sashing, borders, and binding
- 5¼ yards of fabric for backing
- 75" × 94" piece of batting

Cutting

All measurements include ¼" seam allowances. As you cut, keep like fabrics together.

From *each* of the assorted light prints, cut:

1 square, 9¼" × 9¼" (12 total); cut into quarters diagonally to yield 4 large triangles (48 total)

8 squares, 2⅞" × 2⅞" (96 total); cut in half diagonally to yield 16 small triangles (192 total)

4 squares, 2½" × 2½" (48 total)

From *each* of the assorted dark prints, cut:

2 squares, 4⅞" × 4⅞" (24 total); cut in half diagonally to yield 4 large triangles (48 total)

12 squares, 2⅞" × 2⅞" (144 total); cut in half diagonally to yield 16 small triangles (288 total)

From the remaining assorted dark prints, cut a *total* of:

20 squares, 2¾" × 2¾"; cut into quarters diagonally to yield 80 A triangles

From the gray print, cut:

3 strips, 9¼" × 42"; crosscut into 12 squares, 9¼" × 9¼". Cut into quarters diagonally to yield 48 triangles.

From the blue solid, cut:

24 strips, 3½" × 42"; crosscut *16 of the strips* into 31 strips, 3½" × 16½"

2 strips, 2¾" × 42"; crosscut into 20 squares, 2¾" × 2¾". Cut into quarters diagonally to yield 80 A triangles.

3 strips, 2⅜" × 42"; crosscut into 40 squares, 2⅜" × 2⅜". Cut in half diagonally to yield 80 B triangles.

8 strips, 2¼" × 42"

Pieced by Connie Tesene; quilted by Marian Enabnit

Making the Blocks

Press seam allowances in the directions indicated by the arrows.

1 Sew a light small triangle to a dark small triangle to make a half-square-triangle unit. Make 192 units measuring 2½" square, including seam allowances.

Make 192 units,
2½" × 2½".

2 Join one dark small triangle, two triangle units from step 1, and one light square to make a unit. The light print should be the same throughout. Make 48 A units.

Make 48 A units.

3 Join one dark small triangle and two triangle units from step 1 to make a unit. Make 48 B units.

Make 48 B units.

4 Lay out one A unit, one B unit, and one dark large triangle as shown. Join all the pieces to make a triangle unit. Make 12 sets of four matching units (48 total).

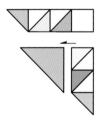 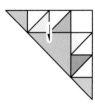

Make 12 sets of
4 matching units.

5 Join a light large triangle and a gray triangle along the short edges as shown. Sew the unit to the long side of a unit from step 4. Make 12 sets of four matching quarter-block units measuring 8½" square, including seam allowances.

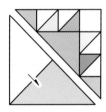 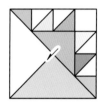

Make 12 sets of
4 matching units,
8½" × 8½".

6 Lay out four matching units from step 5 in two rows as shown. Sew the units into rows and then join the rows to make a block. Make 12 blocks measuring 16½" square, including seam allowances.

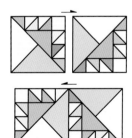 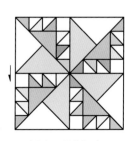

Make 12 blocks,
16½" × 16½".

Assembling the Quilt Top

1 Lay out one blue A triangle, one dark A triangle, and one blue B triangle as shown. Join the A triangles and then sew the B triangle to the long side of the unit. Make 20 sets of four matching units (80 total) measuring 2" square, including seam allowances.

Make 20 sets of
4 matching units,
2" × 2".

2 Lay out four matching units from step 1 in two rows as shown. Sew the units into rows and then join the rows to make a pinwheel unit. Make 20 units measuring 3½" square, including seam allowances.

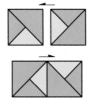

Make 20 units,
3½" × 3½".

3 Join four pinwheel units and three blue 3½" × 16½" strips to make a sashing row. Make five rows measuring 3½" × 60½", including seam allowances.

Make 5 sashing rows,
3½" × 60½".

4 Join four blue 3½" × 16½" strips and three blocks to make a block row. Make four rows measuring 16½" × 60½", including seam allowances.

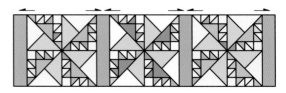

Make 4 block rows,
16½" × 60½".

5 Join the sashing and block rows, alternating them as shown in the quilt assembly diagram below. The quilt-top center should measure 60½" × 79½", including seam allowances.

6 Join the remaining blue 3½"-wide strips end to end. From the pieced strip, cut two 85½"-long strips and two 60½"-long strips. Sew the shorter strips to the top and bottom of the quilt center. Sew the longer strips to the left and right sides. The quilt top should measure 66½" × 85½".

Finishing the Quilt

Visit ShopMartingale.com/HowtoQuilt for free downloadable information on any finishing steps.

1 Layer the quilt top with batting and backing. Baste the layers together.

2 Quilt by hand or machine. The quilt shown is machine quilted with an allover swirl design.

3 Use the blue 2¼"-wide strips to make double-fold binding. Attach the binding to the quilt.

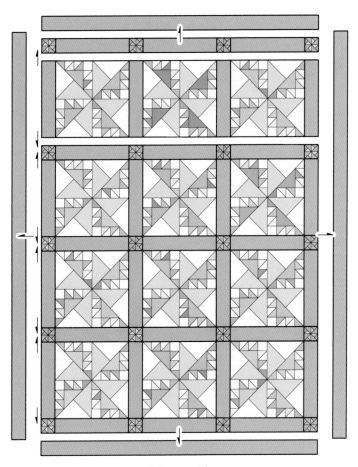

Quilt assembly

Picnic

FINISHED QUILT: 48¼" × 48¼"   FINISHED BLOCK: 8" × 8"

Whether you take this quilt on your next picnic or use it as a table topper or wall quilt at home, it's sure to please. We chose one of our favorite colors, red, for all the prints, but it would look just as lovely in shades of blue or whatever your favorite color is.

Materials

Yardage is based on 42"-wide fabric.

- 1½ yards *total* of assorted light prints for blocks
- 1½ yards *total* of assorted red and pink prints (referred to collectively as "red") for blocks
- 6 squares, 10" × 10", of assorted light florals and checks for Delectable Mountain blocks
- ⅓ yard of red floral for Star blocks
- ⅓ yard of red print for border
- ½ yard of red print for binding
- 3⅛ yards of fabric for backing
- 55" × 55" piece of batting

Cutting

All measurements include ¼" seam allowances.

Delectable Mountain Blocks

From the assorted light prints, cut a *total* of:

56 squares, 2⅞" × 2⅞"; cut in half diagonally to yield 112 triangles

28 squares, 2½" × 2½"

From the assorted red prints, cut a *total* of:

14 squares, 4⅞" × 4⅞"; cut in half diagonally to yield 28 large triangles

84 squares, 2⅞" × 2⅞"; cut in half diagonally to yield 168 small triangles

From *each* of the 6 light florals and checks, cut:

1 square, 8⅞" × 8⅞"; cut in half diagonally to yield 2 triangles (12 total)

Star Blocks

From the assorted light prints, cut *matching sets* of:

12 sets of 4 pieces, 2½" × 4½" (48 total)

12 sets of 4 squares, 2½" × 2½" (48 total)

From the assorted red prints, cut:

12 sets of 8 matching squares, 2½" × 2½" (96 total)

From the red floral, cut:

2 strips, 4½" × 42"; crosscut into 12 squares, 4½" × 4½"

Border and Binding

From the red print for border, cut:

5 strips, 1¾" × 42"

From the red print for binding, cut:

6 strips, 2¼" × 42"

Pieced and quilted by Mary Etherington

Making the
Delectable Mountain Blocks

Press seam allowances in the directions indicated
by the arrows.

1 Sew a light triangle to a red small triangle to
make a half-square-triangle unit. Make 112 units
measuring 2½" square, including seam allowances.

Make 112 units,
2½" × 2½".

2 Join one red small triangle, two triangle units
from step 1, and one light square to make a unit.
Make 28 A units.

Make 28 A units.

3 Join one red small triangle and two triangle units
from step 1 to make a unit. Make 28 B units.

Make 28 B units.

4 Lay out one A unit, one B unit, and one red large
triangle as shown. Join all the pieces to make a
half block. Make 28 half blocks.

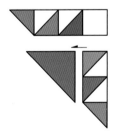 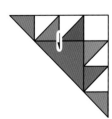

Make 28 half blocks.

5 Sew a light floral or check triangle to the long
side of a half block from step 4. Make 12
Delectable Mountain blocks measuring 8½" square,
including seam allowances. Set aside the remaining
half blocks for the quilt assembly.

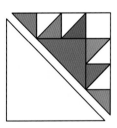 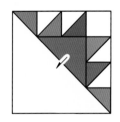

Make 12
Delectable Mountain blocks,
8½" × 8½".

Making the Star Blocks

1 Select four matching light 2½" × 4½" pieces and eight matching red 2½" squares. Draw a diagonal line on the wrong side of each red square. Place a marked square on one end of a light piece, right sides together. Sew on the marked line. Trim the outside corner of the square ¼" from the stitched line. Place a marked square on the opposite end of the light piece. Sew and trim as before to make a flying-geese unit measuring 2½" × 4½", including seam allowances. Make 12 sets of four matching units.

Make 12 sets of
4 matching units,
2½" × 4½".

2 Lay out four matching light squares, four matching flying-geese units, and one red floral square in three rows. Sew all the pieces into rows and then join the rows. Make 12 Star blocks measuring 8½" square, including seam allowances.

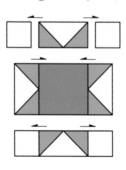 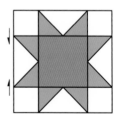

Make 12 blocks,
8½" × 8½".

Assembling the Quilt Top

1 Referring to the quilt assembly diagram below, arrange the Delectable Mountain and Star blocks in diagonal rows, adding the half blocks to the ends of each row as indicated. Sew the blocks and half blocks into rows and then join the rows. The quilt top should measure 45¾" square, including seam allowances.

2 Join the red 1¾"-wide strips end to end. From the pieced strip, cut two 48¼"-long strips and two 45¾"-long strips. Sew the shorter strips to the top and bottom of the quilt center. Sew the longer strips to the left and right sides. The quilt top should measure 48¼" square.

Finishing the Quilt

Visit ShopMartingale.com/HowtoQuilt for free downloadable information on any finishing steps.

1 Layer the quilt top with the batting and backing. Baste the layers together.

2 Quilt by hand or machine. The quilt shown is machine quilted with horizontal straight lines.

3 Use the red 2¼"-wide strips to make double-fold binding. Attach the binding to the quilt.

Quilt assembly

Grape Leaves & Figs

FINISHED QUILT: 52½" × 52½"   FINISHED BLOCK: 12" × 12"

Mother Nature supplies a great deal of inspiration when it comes to color palettes for our quilts. And the rich colors of autumn are ripe with options. To keep your green, gold, and purple palette from being too subdued, don't hesitate to toss in a few sparklers that are a shade or two lighter and brighter.

Materials

Yardage is based on 42"-wide fabric.

- 1¾ yards *total* of assorted light prints for blocks and border
- 1¼ yards *total* of assorted light green prints for blocks and border
- 1¼ yards *total* of assorted dark green prints for blocks and border
- ½ yard *total* of assorted light purple prints for blocks and border
- ½ yard *total* of assorted dark purple prints for blocks and border
- ½ yard *total* of assorted gold prints for blocks and border
- ½ yard of green print for binding
- 3⅜ yards of fabric for backing
- 59" × 59" piece of batting
- 2" finished triangle papers (optional)*

See "Using Triangle Papers" on page 46 before cutting fabrics.

Cutting

All measurements include ¼" seam allowances. Refer to the photo on page 49 for guidance with fabric placement as needed.

Cutting for 1 Green A Block

Cut 4 blocks total.

From 1 light print, cut:

4 squares, 2⅞" × 2⅞"; cut in half diagonally to yield 8 triangles

4 pieces, 2½" × 4½"

From 1 light green print, cut:

1 square, 4½" × 4½"

8 squares, 2½" × 2½"

From 1 dark green print, cut:

6 squares, 2⅞" × 2⅞"; cut in half diagonally to yield 12 triangles

4 pieces, 2½" × 4½"

From 1 dark purple print, cut:

2 squares, 2⅞" × 2⅞"; cut in half diagonally to yield 4 triangles

4 squares, 2½" × 2½"

Continued on page 46

Continued from page 45

Cutting for 1 Green B Block

Cut 8 blocks total.

From *1* light print, cut:

4 squares, 2⅞" × 2⅞"; cut in half diagonally to yield 8 triangles

4 pieces, 2½" × 4½"

From *1* light green print, cut:

1 square, 4½" × 4½"

8 squares, 2½" × 2½"

From *1* dark green print, cut:

6 squares, 2⅞" × 2⅞"; cut in half diagonally to yield 12 triangles

4 pieces, 2½" × 4½"

From *1* gold print, cut:

2 squares, 2⅞" × 2⅞"; cut in half diagonally to yield 4 triangles

4 squares, 2½" × 2½"

Cutting for 1 Purple C Block

Cut 4 blocks total.

From *1* light print, cut:

4 squares, 2⅞" × 2⅞"; cut in half diagonally to yield 8 triangles

4 pieces, 2½" × 4½"

From *1* light purple print, cut:

1 square, 4½" × 4½"

8 squares, 2½" × 2½"

From *1* dark purple print, cut:

6 squares, 2⅞" × 2⅞"; cut in half diagonally to yield 12 triangles

4 pieces, 2½" × 4½"

From *1* dark green print, cut:

2 squares, 2⅞" × 2⅞"; cut in half diagonally to yield 4 triangles

4 squares, 2½" × 2½"

Cutting for Border and Binding

From the assorted light prints, cut a *total* of:

16 strips, 2½" × 8½"

18 squares, 2⅞" × 2⅞"; cut in half diagonally to yield 36 triangles

From the assorted light and dark purple prints, cut a *total* of:

6 squares, 2⅞" × 2⅞"; cut in half diagonally to yield 12 triangles

From the assorted light and dark green prints, cut a *total* of:

3 squares, 2⅞" × 2⅞"; cut in half diagonally to yield 6 triangles

From the assorted gold prints, cut a *total* of:

9 squares, 2⅞" × 2⅞"; cut in half diagonally to yield 18 triangles

From the green print for binding, cut:

6 strips, 2¼" × 42"

Using Triangle Papers

If you use 2" triangle papers, do not cut the light, green, purple, and gold 2⅞" squares. Instead skip steps 1 and 2 of "Making the Green A Blocks," "Making the Green B Blocks," "Making the Purple C Blocks," and step 2 of "Assembling the Quilt Top" (pages, 47, 48, 50, and 51), and follow the directions on the package to cut the pieces and make the half-square-triangle units.

Making the Green A Blocks

Select the pieces cut from one light print, one light green, one dark green, and one dark purple print. Instructions are for making one block; repeat to make a total of four blocks. Press seam allowances in the directions indicated by the arrows.

1 Sew a light triangle to a dark green triangle to make a half-square-triangle unit. Make eight light/dark green units measuring 2½" square, including seam allowances.

Make 8 units,
2½" × 2½".

2 Sew a dark purple triangle to a dark green triangle to make a half-square-triangle unit. Make four dark purple/dark green units measuring 2½" square, including seam allowances.

Make 4 units,
2½" × 2½".

3 Lay out two light/green units from step 1, one purple/green unit from step 2, and one purple square in two rows. Sew all the pieces into rows. Join the rows to make a corner unit. Make four units measuring 4½" square, including seam allowances.

Make 4 units,
4½" × 4½".

4 Draw a diagonal line from corner to corner on the wrong side of the light green 2½" squares. Place a marked square on one end of a dark green 2½" × 4½" piece, right sides together. Sew on the marked line. Trim the outside corner of the square ¼" from the stitched line. Place a marked square on the opposite end of the dark green piece. Sew and

trim as before to make a flying-geese unit that measures 2½" × 4½", including seam allowances. Make four units.

Make 4 units,
2½" × 4½".

5 Sew a flying-geese unit to a light 2½" × 4½" piece to make a side unit. Make four units measuring 4½" square, including seam allowances.

Make 4 units,
4½" × 4½".

6 Lay out four corner units, four side units, and one light green 4½" square in three rows as shown. Sew all the pieces into rows and then join the rows. Make four green A blocks measuring 12½" square, including seam allowances.

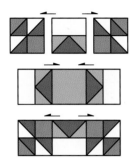

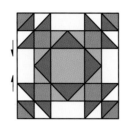

Make 4 green A blocks,
12½" × 12½".

Making the Green B Blocks

Select the pieces cut from one light print, one light green, one dark green, and one gold print. Instructions are for making one block; repeat to make a total of eight blocks. Press seam allowances in the directions indicated by the arrows.

1 Sew a light triangle to a dark green triangle to make a half-square-triangle unit. Make eight light/green units measuring 2½" square, including seam allowances.

Make 8 units,
2½" × 2½".

2 Sew a gold triangle to a dark green triangle to make a half-square-triangle unit. Make four gold/green units measuring 2½" square, including seam allowances.

Make 4 units,
2½" × 2½".

3 Lay out two light/green units from step 1, one gold/green unit from step 2, and one gold square in two rows. Sew all the pieces into rows. Join the rows to make a corner unit. Make four units measuring 4½" square, including seam allowances.

Make 4 units,
4½" × 4½".

4 Using the light green 2½" squares and dark green pieces, repeat step 4 of "Making the Green A Blocks" on page 47 to make four flying-geese units measuring 2½" × 4½", including seam allowances.

Make 4 units,
2½" × 4½".

5 Join the flying-geese units and light 2½" × 4½" pieces to make four side units measuring 4½" square, including seam allowances.

Make 4 units,
4½" × 4½".

Pieced by Connie Tesene; quilted by Calico Hutch

Making the Purple C Blocks

Select the pieces cut from one light print, one light purple, one dark purple, and one dark green print. Instructions are for making one block; repeat to make a total of four blocks. Press seam allowances in the directions indicated by the arrows.

1 Sew a light triangle to a dark purple triangle to make a half-square-triangle unit. Make eight light/purple units measuring 2½" square, including seam allowances.

Make 8 units,
2½" × 2½".

2 Sew a dark green triangle to a dark purple triangle to make a half-square-triangle unit. Make four green/purple units measuring 2½" square, including seam allowances.

Make 4 units,
2½" × 2½".

3 Lay out two light/purple units from step 1, one green/purple unit from step 2, and one dark green square in two rows. Sew all the pieces into rows. Join the rows to make a corner unit. Make four units measuring 4½" square, including seam allowances.

Make 4 units,
4½" × 4½".

6 Lay out four corner units, four side units, and one light green 4½" square in three rows as shown. Sew all the pieces into rows and then join the rows. Make eight green B blocks measuring 12½" square, including seam allowances.

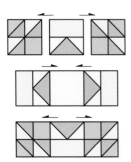 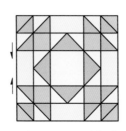

Make 8 green B blocks,
12½" × 12½".

4 Using the light purple 2½" squares and dark purple pieces, repeat step 4 of "Making the Green A Blocks" to make four flying-geese units measuring 2½" × 4½", including seam allowances.

Make 4 units,
2½" × 4½".

5 Join the flying-geese units and light 2½" × 4½" pieces to make four side units measuring 4½" square, including seam allowances.

Make 4 units,
4½" × 4½".

6 Lay out four corner units, four side units, and one light purple 4½" square in three rows as shown. Sew all the pieces into rows and then join the rows. Make four purple C blocks measuring 12½" square, including seam allowances.

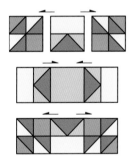 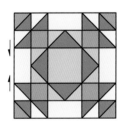

Make 4 purple C blocks,
12½" × 12½".

Assembling the Quilt Top

1 Referring to the quilt assembly diagram on page 52, lay out the blocks in four rows of four blocks each. Sew the blocks into rows and then join the rows. The quilt center should measure 48½" square, including seam allowances.

2 Sew a light triangle to a purple triangle to make a half-square-triangle unit. Make 12 purple units measuring 2½" square, including seam allowances. Repeat to make six green units and 18 gold units.

Make 12 units,
2½" × 2½".

Make 6 units,
2½" × 2½".   Make 18 units,
2½" × 2½".

3 Sew gold units from step 2 to both ends of a light 2½" × 8½" strip to make a border unit. Make eight border units. Set aside the remaining two triangle units for step 5.

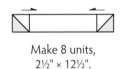

Make 8 units,
2½" × 12½".

4 Repeat step 3 using the purple and green units from step 2 to make the number of border units indicated in the color combinations shown. Set aside the remaining purple unit and green unit for step 5.

Make 3 units,
2½" × 12½".   Make 3 units,
2½" × 12½".

Make 2 units,
2½" × 12½".

5 On a design wall or floor, arrange the border units around the perimeter of the quilt top, making sure like colors are diagonally opposite from each other as shown in the quilt assembly diagram. Place the four remaining triangle units at the ends of the top and bottom borders. Join four border units to make a side border measuring 2½" × 48½". Make two. Make two more borders in the same way, adding a half-square-triangle unit to each end. The top and bottom borders should measure 2½" × 52½", including seam allowances.

Make 2 side borders,
2½" × 48½".

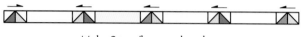

Make 2 top/bottom borders,
2½" × 52½".

6 Sew the shorter borders to the left and right sides of the quilt top. Sew the longer borders to the top and bottom edges. The quilt top should measure 52½" square.

Finishing the Quilt

Visit ShopMartingale.com/HowtoQuilt for free downloadable information on any finishing steps.

1 Layer the quilt top with batting and backing. Baste the layers together.

2 Quilt by hand or machine. The quilt shown is machine quilted with an allover double loop design.

3 Use the green 2¼"-wide strips to make double-fold binding. Attach the binding to the quilt.

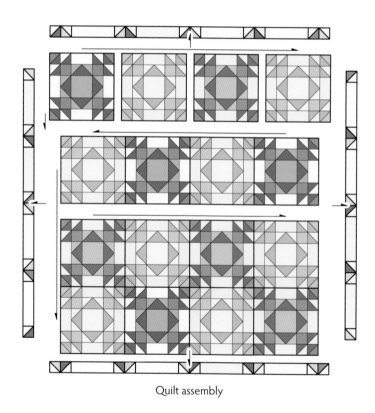

Quilt assembly

Grape Leaves & Figs Pillow

Propped into a decor vignette, or filled with crushed walnut shells to create a jumbo pincushion, a little pillow is the perfect way to use a practice block.

FINISHED PILLOW: 8" × 8"   FINISHED BLOCK: 6" × 6"

Pieced and quilted by Connie Tesene

Materials

- 1 piece of cream print, 4" × 12", for block
- 1 piece of dark red floral, 4" × 12", for block
- 1 piece of light red floral, 5" × 9", for block
- 1 piece of gray print, 4" × 12", for block and border
- 1 piece of red stripe, 7" × 8", for border
- 1 square of fabric, 10" × 10", for pillow back
- 2 squares of batting, 10" × 10"
- Sawdust or polyester fiberfill for stuffing
- 1" finished triangle papers (optional)*

If you use triangle papers, do not cut the cream, red, and gray 1⅞" squares. Instead, skip step 1 of "Making the Green A Blocks" on page 47 and follow the directions on the package to cut the pieces and make the half-square-triangle units.

Cutting

All measurements include ¼" seam allowances.

From the cream print, cut:

4 squares, 1⅞" × 1⅞"; cut in half diagonally to yield 8 triangles (A)

4 pieces, 1½" × 2½" (G)

From the dark red floral, cut:

6 squares, 1⅞" × 1⅞"; cut in half diagonally to yield 12 triangles (B)

4 pieces, 1½" × 2½" (F)

From the light red floral, cut:

8 squares, 1½" × 1½" (E)

1 square, 2½" × 2½" (H)

From the gray print, cut:

2 squares, 1⅞" × 1⅞"; cut in half diagonally to yield 4 triangles (C)

8 squares, 1½" × 1½" (D)

From the red stripe, cut:

4 pieces, 1½" × 6½" (I)

Assembling and Finishing the Pillow

1   Referring to "Making the Green A Blocks" on page 47 for detailed instructions and

illustrations, use the A–H pieces to make one block. The block should measure 6½" square, including seam allowances.

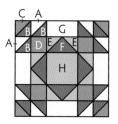

Make 1 block,
6½" × 6½".

2   Sew I strips to the left and right sides of the block. Sew a D square to both ends of the two remaining I strips. Sew these strips to the top and bottom edges. The pillow top should measure 8½" square.

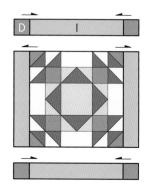

Pillow-top assembly

3   Layer the pillow top with batting and machine quilt horizontal lines through the center. Stitch two diagonal lines. Trim the batting even with the pillow top.

4   Layer the pillow back with batting and machine quilt as desired. Trim the pillow back to the same size as the pillow top.

5   Place the pillow top and back right sides together. Using a ¼" seam allowance, stitch around the perimeter, leaving a 2" opening along the bottom edge.

6   Turn the pillow right side out. Use a large knitting needle or crochet hook to carefully push out the corners. Stuff the pillow to the desired firmness.

7   Slip-stitch the opening closed.

Garden Path

FINISHED QUILT: 44½" × 44½"   FINISHED BLOCK: 12" × 12"

If you're like us, every season is garden season. We're either preparing the soil, planting, cultivating, harvesting, cleaning, or dreaming about what next year's garden will include. Quilting can be much the same as you plan your next project, have several in the works, or imagine what's ahead. Enjoy it all!

Materials

Yardage is based on 42"-wide fabric. Fat eighths measure 9" × 21". Fat quarters measure 18" × 21".

- 9 fat quarters of assorted light prints for blocks and cornerstones
- 9 fat eighths of assorted red prints for blocks
- 1 fat eighth of gray floral for blocks
- ⅜ yard of red stripe for sashing
- ¾ yard of red print for outer border and binding
- 2⅞ yards of fabric for backing
- 51" × 51" piece of batting
- 2" finished triangle papers (optional)*

See "Using Triangle Papers" on page 57 before cutting fabrics.

Cutting

All measurements include ¼" seam allowances.

From *each* of the assorted light prints, cut:

4 squares, 2⅞" × 2⅞"; cut in half diagonally to yield 8 triangles (72 total; A)

8 squares, 2½" × 2½" (72 total; C)

4 squares, 4½" × 4½" (36 total; E)

From *each* of the assorted red prints, cut:

4 squares, 2⅞" × 2⅞"; cut in half diagonally to yield 8 triangles (72 total; B)

8 squares, 2½" × 2½" (72 total; D)

2 pieces, 1½" × 2½" (18 total; G)

2 pieces, 1½" × 4½" (18 total; H)

From the gray floral, cut:

9 squares, 2½" × 2½" (F)

From *1* of the assorted light prints, cut:

8 squares, 2½" × 2½"

From the red stripe, cut:

4 strips, 2½" × 42"; crosscut into 12 strips, 2½" × 12½"

From the red print, cut:

4 strips, 2½" × 40½"

5 strips, 2¼" × 42"

Using Triangle Papers

If you use 2" triangle papers, do not cut the light and red 2⅞" squares. Instead, skip step 1 of "Making the Blocks" above right and follow the directions on the package to cut the pieces and make the half-square-triangle units.

Making the Blocks

Press seam allowances in the directions indicated by the arrows.

1 Sew an A triangle to a B triangle to make a half-square-triangle unit. Make nine sets of eight matching units measuring 2½" square, including seam allowances.

Make 9 sets of
8 matching units,
2½" × 2½".

2 Lay out two units from step 1 and two C squares in two rows as shown. Sew the pieces into rows and then join the rows to make a corner unit. Make nine sets of four matching units measuring 4½" square, including seam allowances.

Make 9 sets of
4 matching units,
4½" × 4½".

3 Draw a diagonal line from corner to corner on the wrong side of the D squares. Place a marked square on one corner of an E piece, right sides together. Sew on the marked line. Trim the excess corner fabric of the square ¼" from the stitched line. Place a marked square on an adjacent corner of the E piece. Sew and trim as before to make a side unit. Make nine sets of four matching units measuring 4½" square, including seam allowances.

Make 9 sets of
4 matching units,
4½" × 4½".

4 Sew G pieces to the top and bottom edges of an F square. Sew H pieces to the left and right sides to make a center unit. Make nine units measuring 4½" square, including seam allowances.

Make 9 units,
4½" × 4½".

5 Lay out four corner units, four side units, and one center unit. The red and light prints should be the same throughout. Sew the units into rows and then join the rows. Make nine blocks measuring 12½" square, including seam allowances.

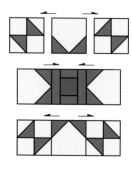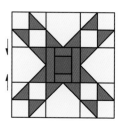

Make 9 blocks,
12½" × 12½".

Assembling the Quilt Top

1 Join three blocks and two red stripe 2½" × 12½" strips to make a block row. Make three rows measuring 12½" × 40½", including seam allowances.

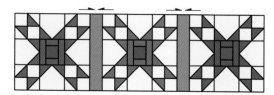

Make 3 block rows,
12½" × 40½".

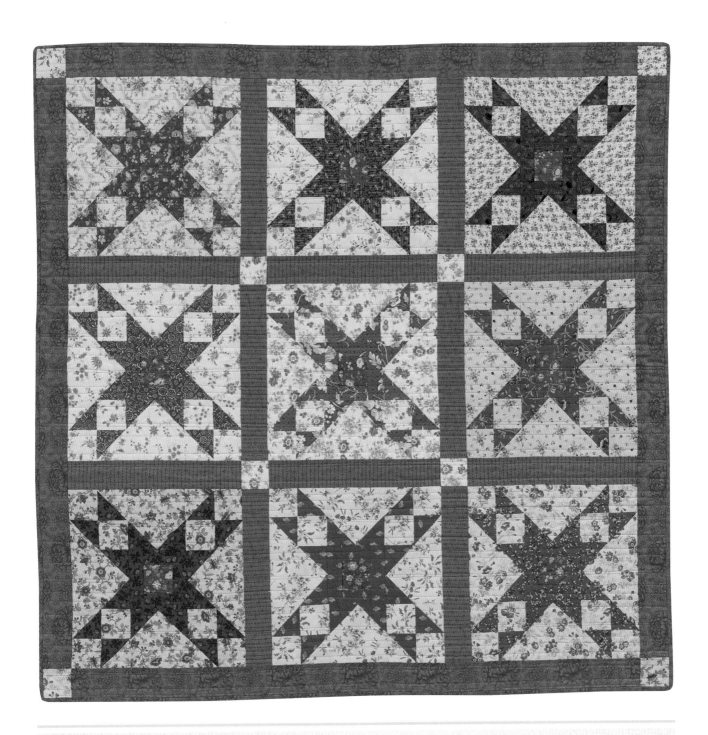

Pieced by Connie Tesene; quilted by Marian Enabnit

2 Join three red stripe 2½" × 12½" strips and two light 2½" squares to make a sashing row. Make two rows measuring 2½" × 40½", including seam allowances.

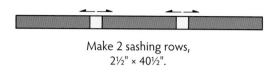

Make 2 sashing rows,
2½" × 40½".

3 Join the block and sashing rows, alternating them as shown below. The quilt top should measure 40½" square, including seam allowances.

4 Sew red 2½" × 40½" strips to the left and right sides of the quilt top. Sew light 2½" squares to both ends of each remaining red 2½" × 40½" strip. Sew these strips to the top and bottom edges. The quilt top should measure 44½" square.

Finishing the Quilt

Visit ShopMartingale.com/HowtoQuilt for free downloadable information on any finishing steps.

1 Layer the quilt top with batting and backing. Baste the layers together.

2 Quilt by hand or machine. The quilt shown is machine quilted with horizontal lines from edge to edge.

3 Use the red print 2¼"-wide strips to make double-fold binding. Attach the binding to the quilt.

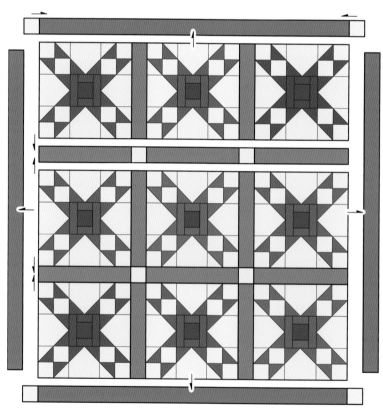

Quilt assembly

Garden Path Pillow

No matter where your path leads, be sure to take time and smell the roses along the way. Finding beauty in everyday moments is often overlooked.

FINISHED PILLOW: 8" × 8"   FINISHED BLOCK: 6" × 6"

Pieced and quilted by Connie Tesene

Materials

Fat eighths measure 9" × 21".

- 1 fat eighth of tan print for block
- 1 fat eighth of red print for block and border
- 1 piece of cream print, 4" × 7", for block
- 1 piece of dark red print, 4" × 5", for block and border
- 1 square of fabric, 10" × 10", for pillow back
- 2 squares of batting, 10" × 10"
- Sawdust or polyester fiberfill for stuffing
- 1" finished triangle papers (optional)*

If you use triangle papers, do not cut the tan and red 1⅞" triangles. Instead see "Using Triangle Papers" on page 57 before cutting the fabrics.

Cutting

All measurements include ¼" seam allowances.

From the tan print, cut:

4 squares, 1⅞" × 1⅞"; cut in half diagonally to yield 8 triangles (A)

4 squares, 2½" × 2½" (E)

From the red print, cut:

4 squares, 1⅞" × 1⅞"; cut in half diagonally to yield 8 triangles (B)

8 squares, 1½" × 1½" (D)

2 pieces, 1" × 1½" (G)

2 pieces, 1" × 2½" (H)

4 strips, 1½" × 6½" (I)

From the cream print, cut:

8 squares, 1½" × 1½" (C)

From the dark red print, cut:

5 squares, 1½" × 1½" (F)

Assembling and Finishing the Pillow

1 Referring to "Making the Blocks" on page 57 for detailed instructions and illustrations, use the

A–G pieces to make one block. The block should measure 6½" square, including seam allowances.

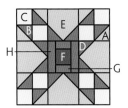

Make 1 block,
6½" × 6½".

2 Sew I strips to the left and right sides of the block. Sew F squares to both ends of the two remaining I strips. Sew these strips to the top and bottom edges. The pillow top should measure 8½" square.

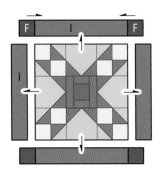

Pillow-top assembly

3 Layer the pillow top with batting and machine quilt with horizontal lines from edge to edge. Trim the batting even with the pillow top.

4 Layer the pillow back with batting and machine quilt as desired. Trim the pillow back to the same size as the pillow top.

5 Place the pillow top and back right sides together. Using a ¼" seam allowance, stitch around the perimeter, leaving a 2" opening along the bottom edge.

6 Turn the pillow right side out. Use a large knitting needle or crochet hook to carefully push out the corners. Stuff the pillow to the desired firmness.

7 Slip-stitch the opening closed.

Fresh Air

FINISHED QUILT: 51½" × 64½"   **FINISHED BLOCK: 12" × 12"**

For years our go-to color palette was dark and dusty, relying heavily on reproduction prints. What a breath of fresh air it is to reinvent ourselves and some of our favorite patterns by creating them in a whole new color palette. It's like getting a fresh start on quilting after all these years!

Materials

Yardage is based on 42"-wide fabric. Fat quarters measure 18" × 21".

- 2½ yards *total* of assorted light prints for blocks and sashing
- 2½ yards *total* of assorted medium and dark prints (referred to collectively as "dark") for blocks and cornerstones
- ½ yard of blue print for binding
- 3¼ yards of fabric for backing
- 58" × 71" piece of batting

Cutting

All measurements include ¼" seam allowances.

For 1 Block

Cut 20 blocks total. Use 1 or 2 light fabrics for each block. Use 4 different dark fabrics for each block. Refer to the photo on page 66 and "Making the Blocks," below right, for guidance with fabric placement as needed.

From 1 light print, cut:

4 matching pieces, 2½" × 4½" (A)

4 matching squares, 2½" × 2½" (B)

4 matching squares, 2⅞" × 2⅞"; cut in half diagonally to yield 8 triangles (D)

From 1 dark print, cut:

4 matching squares, 2½" × 2½" (C)

From 1 dark print, cut:

4 matching squares, 2⅞" × 2⅞"; cut in half diagonally to yield 8 triangles (E)

From 1 dark print, cut:

4 matching pieces, 2½" × 4½" (F)

From 1 dark print, cut:

1 square, 4½" × 4½" (G)

Completing the Quilt

From the assorted light prints, cut a *total* of:

31 strips, 1½" × 12½"

From the assorted dark prints, cut a *total* of:

12 squares, 1½" × 1½"

From the blue print, cut:

7 strips, 2¼" × 42"

Making the Blocks

Instructions are for making one block. Repeat to make a total of 20 blocks. Press seam allowances in the directions indicated by the arrows.

1   Lay out one A piece, one B square, and one C square. Join the B and C squares. Sew the A piece to the left edge to make a corner unit. Make two. Sew the A piece to right edge of the two-patch unit to make two mirror-image units. The units should measure 4½" square, including seam allowances.

Make 2 of each unit,
4½" × 4½".

Pieced and quilted by Mary Etherington

2 Sew a light D triangle to a dark E triangle to make a half-square-triangle unit. Make eight matching units measuring 2½" square, including seam allowances.

Make 8 units,
2½" × 2½".

3 Join two triangle units from step 2 as shown. Sew an F piece to the bottom edge to make a side unit. Make four matching units measuring 4½" square, including seam allowances.

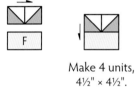

Make 4 units,
4½" × 4½".

4 Lay out four corner units, four side units, and one G square in three rows. Sew all the pieces into rows and then join the rows to make a block. Repeat to make 20 blocks measuring 12½" square, including seam allowances.

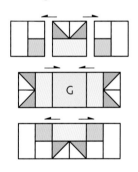
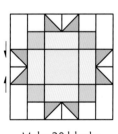

Make 20 blocks,
12½" × 12½".

Assembling the Quilt Top

Refer to the quilt assembly diagram below as needed throughout.

1 Join four blocks and three light 1½" × 12½" strips to make a block row. Make five rows measuring 12½" × 51½", including seam allowances.

2 Join four light 1½" × 12½" strips and three dark 1½" sashing squares to make a sashing row. Make four rows measuring 1½" × 51½", including seam allowances.

3 Join the block and sashing rows, alternating them as shown. The quilt top should measure 51½" × 64½".

Finishing the Quilt

Visit ShopMartingale.com/HowtoQuilt for free downloadable information on any finishing steps.

1 Layer the quilt top with the batting and backing. Baste the layers together.

2 Quilt by hand or machine. The quilt shown is machine quilted with horizontal lines from edge to edge.

3 Use the blue 2¼"-wide strips to make double-fold binding. Attach the binding to the quilt.

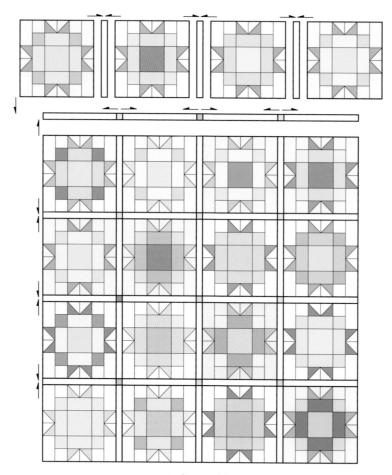

Quilt assembly

Betty's Big Red House

FINISHED QUILT: 34½" × 24½" **FINISHED BLOCK: 26" × 16"**

Sweet Betty is a beautiful black lab and while we may have taken some liberties with just how ornate her house is, we want everyone to know that we love our pets and they'll always have a loving home. Rescue pets, foster pets, lost-and-found pets . . . cats and dogs, we love them all!

Materials

Yardage is based on 42"-wide fabric. Fat quarters measure 18" × 21". Fat eighths measure 9" × 21".

- 7 fat eighths of assorted light prints for block and border
- ½ yard of red print for block, border, and binding
- 5 fat eighths of assorted red prints for block, appliqués, and border
- 8 fat quarters of assorted gray prints for block, appliqués, and border
- 1 fat quarter of light floral for block
- 1 piece, 8" × 9", of black print for dog body
- 1 piece, 3" × 4", of dark gray stripe for dog ear and leg
- ⅞ yard of fabric for backing
- 29" × 39" piece of batting
- Gray embroidery floss for dog eye
- Template plastic

Cutting

All measurements include ¼" seam allowances.

Left Section of Block

From *1* of the light prints, cut:
1 piece, 4½" × 8" (A)
1 strip, 1½" × 9" (B)
1 square, 3½" × 3½" (C)

From *1* of the red fat eighths, cut:
1 piece, 3½" × 4½" (D)
1 strip, 1" × 5" (E)
1 strip, 1½" × 5" (F)

From *1* of the gray prints, cut:
1 strip, 2" × 5" (G)

Center Section of Block

From *1* of the light prints, cut:
2 pieces, 2¾" × 4½" (H)
1 piece, 2½" × 2¾" (I)
2 pieces, 1½" × 1¾" (J)
2 squares, 4½" × 4½" (K)

From *1* of the gray prints, cut:
2 squares, 1½" × 1½" (L)

From *1* of the gray prints, cut:
2 squares, 4½" × 4½" (M)

From the ½ yard of red print, cut:
1 piece, 6¾" × 8½" (N)
2 strips, 1½" × 8" (O)
1 strip, 1" × 8" (P)
1 strip, 1¼" × 8" (Q)
2 pieces, 1¾" × 4¼" (R)

From *1* of the red fat eighths, cut:
1 strip, 1½" × 4½" (U)
3 pieces, 1" × 2¾" (V)
1 piece, 4½" × 7" (W)

From *1* of the light prints, cut:
2 pieces, 1¾" × 4¼" (S)

From *1* of the gray prints, cut:
1 piece, 2¾" × 8" (T)

From *1* of the light prints, cut:
2 pieces, 1¾" × 2¾" (X)

Right Section of Block

From the light floral fat quarter, cut:
1 piece, 10½" × 16½" (Y)

From 1 of the gray prints, cut:
2 pieces, 4" × 5" (Z)

Border and Binding

From the assorted red prints, cut a *total* of:
42 squares, 2½" × 2½"

From the assorted light prints, cut a *total* of:
42 squares, 2½" × 2½"

From the assorted gray prints, cut a *total* of:
42 pieces, 2½" × 4½"

From *1* of the red fat eighths, cut:
4 squares, 4½" × 4½"

From the red print for binding, cut:
4 strips, 1½" × 42"

Making the Left Section

Press seam allowances in the directions indicated by the arrows.

1 Draw a diagonal line from corner to corner on the wrong side of the C square. Place the marked square on one end of the D piece, right sides together. Sew on the marked line. Trim the excess corner fabric of the square ¼" from the stitched line. The unit should measure 3½" × 4½", including seam allowances.

Make 1 unit,
3½" × 4½".

2 Sew an E strip to the left edge of a G strip. Sew an F strip to the right edge of G to make a unit measuring 3½" × 5", including seam allowances.

Make 1 unit,
3½" × 5".

3 Sew the step 2 unit to the red edge of the step 1 unit. Sew a B strip to the left edge and an A piece to the top to make the left section, which should measure 4½" × 16½", including seam allowances.

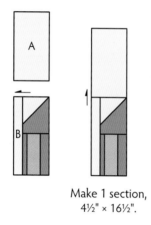

Make 1 section,
4½" × 16½".

Making the Center Section

1 Sew a J piece to an L square. Make two units measuring 1½" × 2¾", including seam allowances.

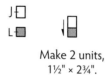

Make 2 units,
1½" × 2¾".

2 Lay out the two H pieces, the two units from step 1, and the I piece as shown. Join the pieces to make the top unit, which should measure 2¾" × 12½", including seam allowances.

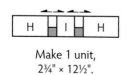

Make 1 unit,
2¾" × 12½".

3 Draw a diagonal line from corner to corner on the wrong side of one K and one M square. Place the marked K square on the upper-left corner of the red N piece, right sides together. Sew on the marked line. Trim the excess corner fabric of the square ¼" from the stitched line. Place the marked M square on the upper-right corner of the N piece. Sew and trim as before to make the roof unit, which should measure 6¾" × 8½", including seam allowances.

Make 1 unit,
6¾" × 8½".

4 Join an R piece to an S piece to make a window unit. Make two units measuring 1¾" × 8", including seam allowances.

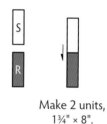

Make 2 units,
1¾" × 8".

5 Lay out the two window units, the O, P, and Q strips, and the T strip as shown. Join the pieces and then sew the unit from step 3 to the top edge. The unit should measure 8½" × 14¼", including seam allowances.

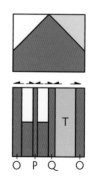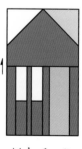

Make 1 unit,
8½" × 14¼".

Pieced and quilted by Connie Tesene

6 Draw a diagonal line from corner to corner on the wrong side of the remaining K square. Layer the marked square on the M square, right sides together. Sew on the marked line. Trim the excess corner fabric of the K square ¼" from the stitched line. Make one half-square-triangle unit measuring 4½" square, including seam allowances.

Make 1 unit,
4½" × 4½".

7 Join the three V pieces and the two X pieces as shown. Sew a U piece to the top edge to make a unit measuring 4½" × 3¾", including seam allowances.

Make 1 unit,
4½" × 3¾".

9 Join the unit from step 8 to the right edge of the unit from step 5. Sew the unit from step 2 to the top edge. The center section should measure 12½" × 16½".

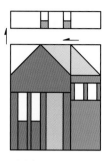

Make 1 section,
12½" × 16½".

Completing the Block

For more details on appliqué and embroidery techniques, visit ShopMartingale.com/HowtoQuilt for free downloadable information.

1 Lay out the left section, center section, and Y piece as shown. Join all the pieces to make a block measuring 26½" × 16½", including seam allowances.

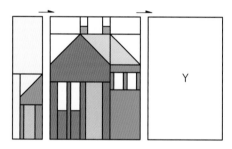

Make 1 block,
26½" × 16½".

2 Using your favorite appliqué method and referring to the patterns on page 79, prepare two small stars, one large star, the tree, and the dog for appliqué.

8 Sew the unit from step 6 to the top of the unit from step 7. Sew the W piece to the bottom to make a unit measuring 4½" × 14¼", including seam allowances.

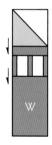

Make 1 unit,
4½" × 14¼".

3 Place the two gray Z pieces right sides together. Sew around the perimeter, leaving a 1" opening for turning along one side. Turn the pieces right side out. Close the opening using a slip stitch.

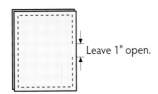

Leave 1" open.

4 Referring to the appliqué placement diagram, appliqué the small stars to the House block. Appliqué the large star to the gray piece from step 3 and then appliqué the gray piece to the background. Appliqué the tree to the house, starting with the tree trunk. Appliqué the dog to the background, starting with the inner back leg. Use the gray floss to cross-stitch the eye on the dog.

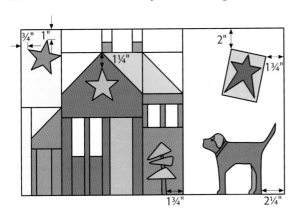

Appliqué placement

Assembling the Quilt Top

1 Draw a diagonal line from corner to corner on the wrong side of the red and light 2½" squares. Place a marked light square on the left end of a gray 2½" × 4½" piece, right sides together. Sew on the marked line. Trim the outside corner of the square ¼" from the stitched line. Place a marked red square on the opposite end of the gray piece. Sew and trim as before to make a flying-geese unit measuring 2½" × 4½", including seam allowances. Make 42 units.

Make 42 units,
2½" × 4½".

2 Join eight flying-geese units to make a side border measuring 4½" × 16½", including seam allowances. Make two. Join 13 flying-geese units and two red 4½" squares to make the top border. Repeat to make the bottom border. The top and bottom borders should measure 4½" × 34½", including seam allowances.

Make 2 side borders,
4½" × 16½".

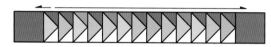

Make 2 top/bottom borders,
4½" × 34½".

3 Sew the shorter borders to the left and right sides of the block. Sew the longer borders to the top and bottom edges. The quilt top should measure 34½" × 24½".

Finishing the Quilt

Visit ShopMartingale.com/HowtoQuilt for free downloadable information on any finishing steps.

1 Layer the quilt top with the batting and backing. Baste the layers together.

2 Quilt by hand or machine. The quilt shown is machine quilted with vertical and horizontal lines in the block. The border is stitched in the ditch around the small triangles and a large X is stitched in the red squares.

3 Use the red 1½"-wide strips to make single-fold binding. Attach the binding to the quilt.

Quilt assembly

Betty's Pillow

Betty the black lab has a special spot in the house for her treats and leash. We whipped up a pillow to mark the location as hers. Adapt the colors to your pet!

FINISHED PILLOW: 9" × 8"

Pieced and quilted by Connie Tesene

Materials

Fat quarters measure 18" × 21".

- 1 piece of light print, 7½" × 8½", for background
- 1 fat quarter of red dot for border and pillow back
- 1 piece of black print, 8" × 9", for dog body
- 1 piece of dark gray stripe, 3" × 4", for dog ear and leg
- 1 piece of red print, 1" × 2½", for dog collar
- 2 pieces of batting, 10" × 11"
- Gray embroidery floss for dog eye
- Sawdust or polyester fiberfill for stuffing
- Template plastic

Cutting

All measurements include ¼" seam allowances.

From the red dot, cut:

1 piece, 10" × 11"

2 strips, 1" × 9½"

2 strips, 1" × 7½"

Making the Pillow

Refer to the photo on page 77 as needed. Press seam allowances in the directions indicated by the arrows.

1 Sew red 1" × 7½" strips to the left and right sides of the light piece. Sew red 1" × 9½" strips to the top and bottom edges. The pillow top should measure 9½" × 8½", including seam allowances.

2 Using your favorite appliqué method and referring to the dog pattern on page 79, prepare the dog for appliqué.

3 Appliqué the dog in the center of the pillow top, starting with the inner-back leg. Use the gray floss to cross-stitch the eye on the dog.

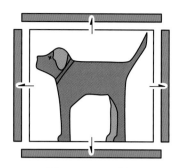

Pillow-top assembly

4 Layer the pillow top with batting and machine quilt the background with horizontal lines from edge to edge. Trim the batting even with the pillow top.

5 Layer the red piece with batting and machine quilt as desired. Trim the pillow back to the same size as the pillow top.

6 Place the pillow top and back right sides together. Using a ¼" seam allowance, stitch around the perimeter, leaving a 2" opening along the bottom edge.

7 Turn the pillow right side out. Use a large knitting needle or crochet hook to carefully push out the corners. Stuff the pillow to the desired firmness.

8 Slip-stitch the opening closed.

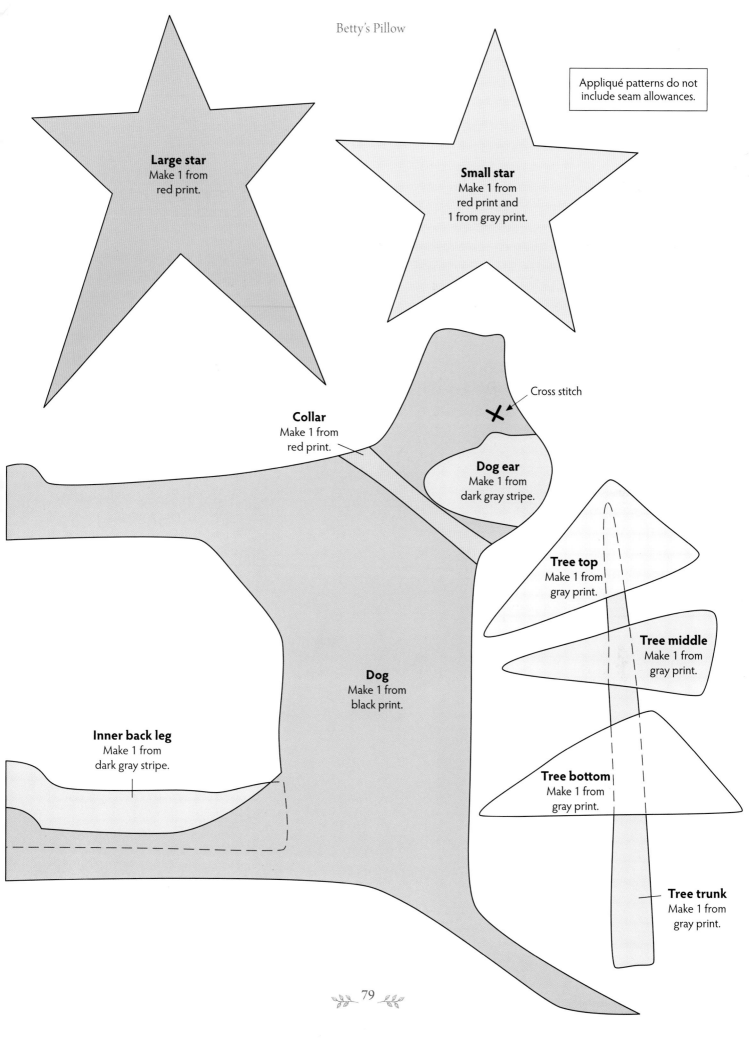

Large star
Make 1 from
red print.

Small star
Make 1 from
red print and
1 from gray print.

Appliqué patterns do not
include seam allowances.

Cross stitch

Collar
Make 1 from
red print.

Dog ear
Make 1 from
dark gray stripe.

Tree top
Make 1 from
gray print.

Tree middle
Make 1 from
gray print.

Dog
Make 1 from
black print.

Inner back leg
Make 1 from
dark gray stripe.

Tree bottom
Make 1 from
gray print.

Tree trunk
Make 1 from
gray print.

About the Authors

Connie Tesene

I started quilting in America's bicentennial year, 1976, and have seen many changes in the quilt industry since then. My first quilt was made with templates cut from cardboard, traced around with a pencil, and cut out with scissors. The rotary cutter hadn't even been invented yet. Wow, times have certainly changed for the better!

Since closing the Country Threads quilt shop in 2014, I've enjoyed the luxury of time—time for gardening, babysitting, dog walking, volunteering, traveling, reading, and, of course, quiltmaking. My husband, Roy, and I still live in the home where we raised our three boys. It's a wonderful house with an extensive garden, but the house is also 120 years old, so it's always in need of work. The garden looks great when you drive by, but don't get too close or you'll see the weeds!

I would like to be remembered as a maker of pies, quilts, gardens, art, fun, and a cozy home.

Mary Etherington

Like Connie, I made my first quilt in the mid 1970s using a cardboard template and scissors to cut all the pieces. When the rotary cutter came along, our quilting lives changed for the better.

My husband, Rick, and I live on the Country Threads farm with goats, geese, fancy chickens, dogs, cats, and two parakeets. I'll be taking care of animals for the rest of my life!

I've been a church pianist for over 60 years, and I play for services and the choir almost every Sunday. I love reading, caring for my extensive collection of cacti and succulents, and quiltmaking.

Connie (*left*) and Mary talk nearly every day and remain best friends. Both have serious fabric addictions, and they both LOVE making quilts! They write a blog post almost every day—follow them for farm news including quilting, gardening, homemaking, and pets. Sign up today!

Visit them at ChickenScratchCountryThreads.com.